FIRE BEHAVIOR

AND

SPRINKLERS

Factory Mutual Engineering Division Fire Test Building, first in use in 1947. This facility, at Norwood, Mass., made possible a large portion of the research and development reported in this book.

FIRE BEHAVIOR
AND
SPRINKLERS

NORMAN J. THOMPSON

NATIONAL FIRE PROTECTION ASSOCIATION
470 Atlantic Ave., Boston, Mass. 02210

Library of Congress Card Number 64-18974

NFPA Number: SPP-2

Standard Book Number 87765-052-7

Printed in U.S.A.

Foreword

Sprinkler protection has proven itself dependable over the years. The fire record leaves no question of the value of sprinklers as a fire extinguishing and control medium. But sprinklers are, nevertheless, only a method of fire protection. They perform efficiently when called upon to the extent that the factors governing their effectiveness in fire extinguishment and control under varied conditions are thoroughly understood by those responsible for their installation and maintenance.

Here is the book that explains the often overlooked fundamentals of fire behavior that are important to a thorough understanding of the capabilities of sprinkler protection. Mr. Thompson, who retired in 1959 as director of the laboratories of the Engineering Division of the Associated Factory Mutual Fire Insurance Companies, at Norwood, Massachusetts, has drawn upon his experience and observations to explain the properties and arrangement of combustibles affecting the growth and spread of fire, the factors influencing the travel of combustion products, and how the location of sprinklers themselves in relation to the combustibles materially affect the operating characteristics and extinguishing capabilities of sprinkler protection.

I would like to emphasize that this is Mr. Thompson's book. His long years of experience in fire and sprinkler protection investigation and experimentation eminently qualify him to write with authority on sprinkler protection. The text has not been acted upon or reviewed by any of the technical committees of the National Fire Protection Association. It is being published by the NFPA as a valued addition to the literature on fire extinguishment and as a tribute to Mr. Thompson's competent and dedicated service to fire protection.

Percy Bugbee, General Manager
National Fire Protection Association

v

Author's Preface

Toward the latter part of my more than 33 years' experience in investigations of industrial fire protection, I became convinced that there was a real need for a text that would explain some of the fundamentals of fire behavior and which would then relate these fundamentals to sprinkler protection so that the action of sprinklers under different fire conditions might be better understood, possibly resulting eventually in improved sprinkler application standards.

It is impossible to cover in detail by rules or standards every conceivable fire condition, but the fire protection engineer who is reasonably familiar with the factors influencing fire intensity and travel of resulting combustion gases, and who at the same time has a good knowledge of what sprinklers can or cannot do under practical conditions, is fairly well equipped to analyze any fire protection problem to good advantage and thereby to recommend effective protection measures. On the other hand, without a proper knowledge of the fundamentals, the fire protection engineer may be considerably handicapped, particularly in the solution of problems involving hazards of more than ordinary severity. Because of a realization that there are many who do not appreciate some of the important factors in designing fire control systems, this book is written with a sincere desire to be of the most practical help.

In order to explain and illustrate the behavior of fires and the action of sprinkler protection, I have drawn freely on the experience and test results obtained from research at the laboratories of the Engineering Division of the Associated Factory Mutual Fire Insurance Companies. Due to the foresight of the Factory Mutual management in making available in 1946 and 1947 the large-scale fire test facilities at Norwood, Massachusetts, and in actively supporting a long-range research program, a large proportion of the fundamental information contained in this book can now be presented. Without such foresight a great deal of the information would still be in the realm of theory or speculation, and the development of the present standard (spray) sprinkler would not have been possible.

Any opinions or conclusions, particularly those which at first may seem novel or even radical, are to be considered as my personal responsibility.

Norman J. Thompson
April 30, 1964

Table of Contents

List of Illustrations

chapter 1

COMBUSTIBLES AND THEIR FUEL PROPERTIES

The inherent properties of a fuel govern the degree of its potential combustibility even though other factors, such as state of division and mechanical arrangement, are important in determining fire hazard. This chapter explains the properties of combustibles which have a direct bearing on their relative fire hazard.

Fires and explosions are with few exceptions oxidation reactions occurring only in the vapor or gaseous phase. Excessive heat is developed by the union of oxygen with vapors or gases from the involved fuels. In most cases, it is oxygen from the air that unites chemically with gaseous fuels or with the vapors from combustible liquids. A few substances, such as pyroxylin, will decompose violently with evolution of heat at some critical temperature without external oxygen; they contain oxygen in their own molecules and are not dependent on air as a source of oxygen for combustion. Reactions other than oxidation which may produce heat to a dangerous degree are the sudden and violent decomposition of explosives, nitric acid on cotton to produce nitrocellulose, water on calcium carbide to produce acetylene, reactions between concentrated acids and alkalies, and reactions between combustible gases and chlorine or fluorine.

As practically all common fires are vapor-phase reactions, the fuel must be present in gaseous form. Many liquids are sufficiently volatile to vaporize readily without added heat. Liquids of lesser volatility and solid combustibles must be heated to temperatures high enough to form vapors or decomposition gases. Once the fuel is present in the gaseous phase, it will mix readily with air by convection or diffusion. If fuel gases in sufficient concentration are present in the vapor-air mixture and an ignition source

1

is available, a fire will result, flashing through the entire volume immediately. If conditions are favorable for continually producing added vaporized fuel, the initial flash will be followed by a fire occurring in the zone where the fuel diffuses and mixes with the air supply.

As vaporization of less volatile liquids and decomposition of solids to generate combustible gases requires added heat to some degree, the generation of gases may be assisted by the state of division of the fuel, e.g., finely atomized liquids and finely ground or pulverized solids. Provided there is a proper mixture with air, the ignition source must be sufficient both in point of temperature and quantity of heat supplied to raise a small volume of the mixture with air to the temperature of active combustion. The first particles of liquid or solid fuel mixed with air will then burn, developing heat which warms up surrounding particles to the combustion temperature; then this process repeats itself and spreads through the entire mixture. A familiar example of this process is the domestic oil burner which uses a liquid fuel with a flash point of 160°F. or higher.

In general, the combustibility and the rate of fire spread are highest in mixtures of gases or vapors with air since a maximum condition of subdivision of fuel and intimacy of mixture with oxygen exists. Fire spread is less rapid in the case of atomized liquids because additional heat is required for vaporization, and, usually, even less rapid for finely divided solids or dusts.

General Classes of Combustibles

A broad classification of fuels into solids, liquids, and gases is a rough guide to the relative hazards of each fuel, and, in a general way, tells whether or not a fire in the fuel can be extinguished by the cooling effect of water from sprinklers. Fires in combustible gases or in some of the more volatile flammable liquids cannot be extinguished by water except in rare circumstances where water is introduced into the combustion zone in the form of a dense, finely divided spray or fog. The steam produced by the vaporization of the water may displace enough oxygen from the atmosphere to prevent combustion from continuing. As a general rule, though, fires in combustible gases or the more volatile flammable liquids cannot be extinguished by water — only the surroundings can be protected from the exposing fire.

Practically all common combustible solids are stable at ordinary temperatures. While some oxidation in a very low degree may occur in the normal temperature range, temperatures considerably above normal are necessary to produce combustible vapors or gases in sufficient concentration to result in a fire. Wood, for example, must be heated to temperatures well above 500°F. to result in fire. The heat may come entirely from an external source or with some assistance from its own oxidation below the fire point.

Combustible liquids may be sufficiently volatile at ordinary temperatures so that their vapors will be present in a flammable concentration when mixed with air, requiring only a very small ignition source, such as a static spark, to produce a fire. Other combustible liquids of lesser volatility must be heated to the upper range of normal temperatures or beyond before a fire can result. Gasoline is probably the most commonly occurring of the first group, whereas heavy fuel oils and the vegetable oils are good examples of the second group.

Combustible Solids

A majority of all common solid combustible materials are mainly cellulosic in nature. These include wood in all its forms, paper and paper products (usually wood products), soft insulating board (generally wood or sugar cane fiber), and the many different vegetable fibers. Other classes of combustible solids are plastics, certain metals that show distinctive fire hazards, and certain other materials which are solid at ordinary room temperatures but which become liquid when heated.

Wood: This class includes all of the natural woods in original solid form, plywood, and wood veneers. The most commonly used of the various kinds of wood are Douglas fir, spruce in variety, Western hemlock, white pine, yellow or Southern pine, white and red oak, maple, beech, birch, cypress, cedar, and redwood. The first five named are generally used for structural elements while the next five are used principally for floors, furniture or for boxes, pallets or other equipment items. The last three, cypress, cedar, and redwood, are quite durable in the presence of moisture so are widely used for shingles and clapboards. Other woods, including walnut, mahogany, teak, cherry, gumwood (tupelo), and basswood (linden), are used mostly for furniture or interior finish. Except possibly for yellow pine, which has a high resin content, these woods are in the same general class from the fire standpoint. While they differ in available heat per pound, in density, thermal conductivity, specific heat, and in their decomposition products, the differences are not great enough to require individual treatment.

Wood in the form of plywood, often with a decorative hard wood surface (veneer), burns somewhat more readily than solid wood on account of the tendency to delaminate under fire exposure. Plaster board made with a thin paper surface on an interior base of gypsum has a relatively low combustibility because of the thinness of the paper. Another composite product has a surface layer of a cement-asbestos composition over an interior of vegetable fiber insulation. Here again the comparative combustibility is low but the insulation will burn with a glowing combustion, so that the overall fire resistance leaves much to be desired. Solid wood, if it is exposed, is generally painted for purposes of both decoration and preservation. Some heavily pigmented paints may increase the resistance to ignition slightly, but in most cases the application of stains, fillers, shellac, paint, varnish or lacquer has a negligible effect on combustibility except for a short period before the finishes have dried or hardened.

Structural wood members may be given a preservative treatment to protect them against the combined action of fungi and moisture. Treatment with zinc chloride salt generally has a marked influence in reducing ease of ignition.

When creosote is used for this purpose, the combustibility may be slightly increased. Compounds based on copper and phenol derivatives make very little difference in combustibility. These treatments to be really effective should be by deep impregnation; mere surface applications are only of temporary value as preservatives.

There are several effective fire retardant treatments by deep impregnation. They protect the wood from active combustion except by rather severe exposures, and even under severe exposure they can reduce the amount of fuel contributed by the wood to the fire. The practical difficulty is in getting a sufficient concentration of the fire retardant to penetrate deeply enough to afford more than a short time delay. Two commercial products in this class have been tested and approved for use under certain prescribed conditions by one or more recognized testing laboratories.

There have been developed over a long period of years many so-called fire retardant paints. However, very few have been effective; and these have been confined mostly to the intumescent type which forms a non-combustible insulating surface layer when exposed to elevated temperatures. These will protect against ignition and fire spread when the igniting exposure is of very short duration or is small and very much localized. If the exposure is enough to produce high temperatures over some little area and the exposure duration is more than a very few minutes, the fire retardant paint protection will amount to little more than a time delay. The effectiveness of all fire retardant paints is increased when applied to soft porous woods such as white pine or low density vegetable fiber insulation boards because of greater penetration below the surface.

Fibers: All textile fibers are combustible to some extent. The natural vegetable fibers are highly flammable if arranged to expose large surfaces to access of air such as would occur with dresses in quantity on display racks. Fortunately a fire under these conditions is usually of short duration on account of the relatively low weight of material involved. The principal commercial vegetable fiber is cotton but there are significant quantities of flax, jute, hemp, ramie, and kapok used. These all have about the same degree of combustibility when present in the same form and arrangement.

The animal fibers are all complex proteins fairly resistant to acids but readily attacked and dissolved by alkalies. They are decidedly less combustible than the vegetable fibers. The most important from the production standpoint is sheep's wool followed by silk. Other animal fibers of commercial importance are those of the alpaca and vicuna, the angora (mohair) and cashmere goats, the camel and the horse. Rabbit, cow and cat hair is used mostly for making fur felts.

Synthetic textile fibers have been developed in considerable numbers but by far the largest production is in viscose rayon which is practically identical chemically to cotton and has about the same fire hazard. Almost all of the other synthetic fibers are in the same general class of combustibility although some are slightly less hazardous than cotton. Exceptions are rayon acetate and synthetic fibers containing nitrogen such as nylon (a poly-amide) ; both of these are decidedly less combustible than cotton fiber.

Plastics: An important class of solid combustible materials may be listed under the general heading of plastics most of which are synthetic. One of the earliest synthetic plastics was pyroxylin developed originally in the search for an ivory substitute. One of its many early uses was as a base for photographic film, but this has been generally superseded by cellulose acetate or "safety" film, because pyroxylin was quite flammable. Bakelite made from phenol and formaldehyde was later developed and is still widely employed for molded articles. Some of the more recently developed plastics include vinyl copolymer, polystyrene, urea-formaldehyde compounds, polyurethane, and compounds based on acrylic acid, polyethylene and polypropylene.

Probably the most widely used of natural plastics is rubber existing as a colloidal suspension in the milky sap or latex from rubber producing plants, the most important of which is *Hevea brasiliensis*. This tree and others of the same genus are cultivated in the rubber plantations of Indonesia, the Malay Peninsula, and Ceylon, which have largely supplanted South America as a source for the original Para rubber from wild trees. Other natural rubber-like substances are gutta-percha and balata both of which are used in electric cable insulation and for golf ball coverings, and substitutes for Para rubber during World War II from the Mexican guayule and the Russian dandelion.

Many types of synthetic rubber are produced in this country, the most important of which is SBR, a copolymer of butadiene and styrene (the type GR-S of World War II). Other types suitable for special purposes are neoprene (poly-chloroprene), Buna-N or nitrile from butadiene and acrylonitrile, butyl rubber from isobutylene with butadiene or isoprene, Koroseal (a polymer of vinyl chloride), and Thiokol (a copolymer of ethylene dichloride and sodium tetrasulfide). By far the highest of these in production is SBR used mainly for automobile tires, followed by Neoprene, and butyl rubber which is widely used for inner tubes. Recently there has been a great deal of development in the so-called stereo synthetic rubbers which are said to equal and may supplant natural rubber. They resemble natural rubber in molecular form; and one of these synthetics, poly-isoprene, is practically the same chemically. Rapidly rising in production is polybutadiene, used mostly in blends with natural rubber or other synthetics for tires.

All of the plastic materials are combustible, varying only in degree. The most flammable, pyroxylin, has been largely supplanted by cellulose acetate which is somewhat less combustible than ordinary paper. The plastics which are more combustible than wood or paper are the various rubbers, both natural and synthetic; and they will ignite at lower temperatures. In the freshly ground or powdered form they are subject to spontaneous heating and ignition at temperatures only slightly above normal. Exceptions are Neoprene and Koroseal which are somewhat less combustible. The synthetic rubbers in the form of automobile tires, especially when in quantities stored in considerable bulk and height, present a potential fire hazard requiring extra strong sprinkler protection. The hazard of natural rubber is about the same except that natural rubber has the added disadvantage that under elevated temperatures it will melt and flow. Rubber and other plastics are made up into foamed products which are somewhat more hazardous than in the solid form. Here again rubber foamed products generally have a greater fire hazard than other plastic foamed products such as polyurethane, since they can be easily ignited by a small ignition source such as a glowing cigarette.

Metals: While metals in general are considered noncombustible, there are a few with distinctive fire hazards. Sodium, potassium, and lithium will burn in air and react violently in contact with water. Magnesium will burn if raised to its melting point, and the burning metal cannot be extinguished by carbon dioxide, vaporizing liquid extinguishers or most common chemical extinguishing agents. Once burning it will react with nitrogen to form magnesium nitride. This reaction is quite mild but still liberates enough heat to maintain the metal at a high temperature. Molten magnesium reacts with water with considerable heat and the generation of hydrogen gas. Unless the water application is very limited and in the form of a very fine spray, the reaction may be of explosive violence.

In addition to those metals already mentioned there are many others which will burn, especially in powdered form. These include aluminum, iron, titanium, and zirconium. Iron can be made to burn in air in the form of fine steel wool especially if contaminated with oil. All of the metals which will burn in the powdered form are capable of causing dust explosions when suspended in air. Of these, two of the most potentially destructive are magnesium and aluminum. Other highly combustible metals with severe dust explosion hazards when in the powdered form are germanium, hafnium, plutonium, titanium, uranium, and zirconium. None of this group, however, have the widespread use of aluminum and magnesium.

Low Melting Point Solids: There is a large class of materials which are solid at ordinary temperatures but melt to liquids at temperatures in the general range of from 100° to 250°F. This class includes animal fats, vegetable and petroleum waxes, petroleum greases, wood and coal tars, greases from oxidation of cooking oils, and pitches, bitumens and asphalt. This class also includes soaps, hydrogenated vegetable oils such as margarine, and a great number of organic chemical compounds. Once raised in temperature to the liquid form, they behave like any high flash point flammable liquids, and from the fire hazard standpoint are treated in the same manner. Even the element sulfur has a low melting point (234°F.).

Liquids

There is a large number of liquid fuels sufficiently volatile to produce flammable vapors in mixture with air at ordinary atmospheric temperatures. Especially volatile are ethyl ether and petroleum ether (mostly pentane). Other common volatile flammable liquids are gasoline, various petroleum naphthas, benzol (benzene), carbon disulfide, and methyl (wood) alcohol. Some paints and lacquers may also contain flammable solvents or thinners. Combustible liquids which require only a small elevation of temperature to burn include petroleum safety solvents, kerosene, light fuel oils, ethyl alcohol and many varnishes, paints and lacquers. Petroleum lubricating oil and all of the natural vegetable oils have flash points in the range of from 400° to 600°F. All common combustible liquids except carbon disulfide are lighter than water, and the vapors of all flammable liquids are heavier than air.

Combustible liquids with flash points well above the normal temperature range will burn without general heating if finely atomized and mixed with air such as is accomplished in the ordinary oil burner. In this case a strong ignition source, such as a hot electric spark, raises the mixture locally to the fire temperature, and the heat from this local combustion serves to heat the surrounding mixture of atomized fuel and air so that the fire may spread and continue even after the spark is discontinued.

Gases

The commonest combustible gases are hydrogen, carbon monoxide, methane (natural gas), the liquefied petroleum gases (propane and butane), ammonia, ethylene, propylene, and acetylene. Of these hydrogen is the lightest of all compared to air, methane and ammonia only slightly more than half as dense as air, and carbon monoxide and acetylene almost as heavy as air. Ethane, propane, and butane are all heavier than air but ethane only slightly heavier. Hydrogen is distinguished by a high rate of diffusibility and a high rate of flame propagation in the proper mixture with air. Acetylene has a high heat of combustion, and mixtures with air or oxygen have a high rate of flame propagation; it is also chemically unstable when compressed and may decompose with explosive violence at pressures less than 30 pounds per square inch. Consequently, acetylene must be stored and shipped dissolved in acetone and distribution and handling is done at pressures not over 15 pounds per square inch. Acetylene is made by the interaction of water and calcium carbide which, oddly enough, in the dry state, is no more combustible than concrete.

Nature of Fuel Properties

While the division of combustibles into three groups (solids, liquids, and gases) gives a rough idea of the hazard, a more precise evaluation of potential hazard requires information on the natural properties of the fuel, such as the melting point or boiling point, the volatility or vapor pressure, the heat of combustion, the chemical instability or reactivity, and the tendency towards auto-oxidation or spontaneous combustion. For the fire protection engineer flash and fire points are especially valuable in assessing the potential hazard of flammable liquids.

The most significant characteristics are:

Physical State: The normal physical state, whether gas, liquid, or solid.

Volatility: The volatility of liquids is important since all flaming fires are reactions between the oxygen of the atmosphere and gaseous products. The volatility is governed primarily by the boiling point, although practically all combustible liquids produce flammable vapors at temperatures well below the boiling point. The boiling point is the temperature at which the vapor pressure of the liquid equals the atmospheric pressure, or at which the liquid more or less rapidly changes to the vapor state.

Heat of Vaporization: The amount of heat which must be put into a liquid in order to convert it to a gas is the heat of vaporization. Expressed in British Thermal Units (btu) per pound it is approximately 970, 367, 160, and 123 for water, ethyl alcohol, pentane, and turpentine respectively, at their boiling points.

Melting Point and Heat of Fusion: For solids, the melting point and the heat of fusion are important since heat is required to make the change from the solid to the liquid state. This required heat is approximately 142 btu per pound at 32°F. for water and 63 btu per pound at 126°F. for paraffin wax. (Note: many solids have appreciable vapor pressures below their melting points, e.g., water in the form of ice and naphthalene which has a flash point of 174°F. and a melting point of 177°F.)

Heat of Decomposition: Almost all solids of vegetable origin, such as wood, paper, and cotton, do not melt but first decompose. Exceptions are vegetable fats, waxes, resins, sugar, and natural rubber. The principal animal fibers such as wool also melt. However, most of these substances undergo some chemical change or decomposition well below the boiling point. In every case the decomposition (pyrolysis) is a rather complex process, and usually char-like substances and gases are formed, some of the latter being liquids at ordinary temperatures. Substances of vegetable and animal origin require an input of heat (heat of decomposition) to bring the change about, but in some cases, wood for example, heat may be given off after certain stages of the decomposition have been reached. Because of the complexity of the decomposition, figures for the heats of decomposition are likely to be somewhat indefinite.

While nearly all combustible materials decompose in an

endothermic reaction (requiring heat to be put into the material), there are a few substances more or less unstable in character which produce heat during decomposition. None of these substances occurs naturally; they are all chemically synthesized, one of the commonest being the gas acetylene, which evolves heat on decomposition equivalent to approximately 3,750 btu per pound or 26 btu per cubic foot (calculated at normal pressure and temperature).

Specific Heat: This figure is the ratio as compared to water of the heat in British thermal units required to raise the temperature of a pound of any substance by 1°F. For the majority of combustibles, the ratio is between one quarter and one half, but there are many exceptions, especially the metals which are lower. Another exception on the high side is ethyl alcohol.

Heat Conductivity: This characteristic property has some influence on the fire hazard because the higher the conductivity the more heat has to be applied to the surface of solid fuel in order to raise it to the fire point and at the same time make up for heat loss to the interior of the fuel mass. This is particularly noticeable in heavy sections of metal. Magnesium, for example, has a conductivity almost 4,000 times that of fir wood (across the grain).

On the other hand, a high heat conductivity facilitates the transfer of heat from an exposure or from a combustion zone to a mixture of unburned gas and air. Thus the rate of flame spread is accelerated. A notable example is the gas hydrogen which in a mixture with air has a high rate of flame propagation. (Note: The thermal conductivity of hydrogen is almost six times that of air.)

Heat of Combustion: The available heat on complete combustion is quite significant but usually is not the most important factor in determining ignition susceptibility or fire intensity, except when the material is very much diluted with inert material such as a structural insulating product consisting of cement and excelsior, or alcohol well diluted with water. A high proportion of inert diluent may reduce the average heat of combustion to a point where the fire hazard is much reduced or even eliminated. Vegetable and mineral oils as well as asphalt, pitch, fats, and waxes have heats of complete combustion ranging from about 15,000 to 20,000 btu per pound. The various species of wood generally are in the range of from 7,000 to 9,000 btu per pound (dry basis).

Auto-oxidation (Spontaneous Heating): Almost all combustible materials of vegetable origin will combine with oxygen at temperatures well below those required for ignition. There are many of animal and mineral origin which usually do so but at somewhat higher temperatures. Even cotton will oxidize very slowly at ordinary temperatures especially in the presence of moisture. Many vegetable oils are particularly prone to spontaneous heating from oxidation when spread over a large surface area such as on textile fibers and when there is a large mass of the oily fiber which provides sufficient insulating effect to retain the heat of oxidation and thus permit temperatures to rise. Green or uncured hay in bulk will heat by the action of micro-organisms to about 160°F. at which point the heating is continued by oxidation, sometimes to ignition. Solid wood will also heat by oxidation at temperatures even below 500°F. and, in the sawdust form, at much lower temperatures. In fact, it may be said of almost all combustibles that they are raised in temperature by oxidation for some few degrees to the actual ignition temperature without benefit of any additional external heat. For this reason, the usual tests for ignition temperature merely show the temperature to which a substance must be raised in order for auto-oxidation to carry the substance further to the actual ignition temperature.

Flash and Fire Points: The properties and characteristics enumerated in the preceding paragraphs are the principal bases for the results of tests for the flash and fire points of substances. The flash point is the temperature to which any substance must be raised in order that, either by vaporization or decomposition or both, a vapor-air mixture will result in a surrounding still atmosphere which will flame temporarily or flash in the presence of an ignition source. The fire point is the temperature, usually higher than the flash point, at which vapors are produced at a rate sufficient to maintain continuous flaming. (The auto-ignition temperature, on the other hand, is the temperature to which a substance or its vapors must be raised to result in flaming or glowing combustion without the help of an external ignition source.) While flash and fire point tests are principally for liquids, they also have significance for solids although the results are much less precise.

Moisture Content: Practically all natural materials of vegetable origin absorb moisture, the degree of absorption depending on the humidity of the surrounding atmosphere. Among them are cotton and other fibers, paper, and the various species of wood which among themselves differ widely in their absorptive tendencies. Moisture content is important from the fire hazard standpoint because heat is needed to evaporate it, and the resultant water vapor dilutes the fuel vapors. In the case of green wood with a high moisture content (25 per cent and upwards), this dilution may be so great that the first products of decomposition may not be capable of flaming combustion. Even in the normal moisture content range (from about 5 to 15 per cent moisture) wood is more resistant to ignition than thoroughly dried wood because of the heat required to evaporate the moisture and because of vapor dilution. Thus with wood having its normal moisture content, original ignition and spread of flame are both slowed down. In practice a substantial moisture content acts principally as a time delay. If there is sufficient heat exposure to compensate, the end result in fire intensity may not be very much different even though fire spread is retarded. The occasional real benefit comes in preventing ignition from exposures, which are either very small or of short duration, but which might ignite very dry material.

Instability or Chemical Reactivity: Under the general heading of hazardous chemicals there are many substances which have properties of instability or chemical reactivity which can lead to fires or explosions. Some materials contain available oxygen, e.g., pyroxylin, while other compounds without oxygen may decompose exothermically, e.g., acetylene and carbon disulfide. There are also many substances, such as quicklime, sodium hydride, concentrated acids, and dry caustics, which react with water to produce considerable amounts of heat. Substances which react vigorously with combustibles include chlorine and fluorine gases and the specially active oxidizing agents such as nitrates, peroxides, perchlorates, and some oxides. Freshly made charcoal and other carbon products have a large capacity for absorbing gases including oxygen from the air. Thus, if not thoroughly cooled before admitting air, a fire may result from auto-oxidation.

There are so many of these hazardous materials requiring special handling and fire prevention methods that it is outside of the scope of this work to give them adequate treatment. The reader is instead referred to the National Fire Protection Association's *Fire Protection Handbook,** the Factory Mutual *Handbook of Industrial Loss Prevention,†* and special safety data sheets available from chemical manufacturers.

Fire Protection Handbook (12th ed.; Boston: National Fire Protection Association, 1962).

†Factory Mutual Engineering Division, *Handbook of Industrial Loss Prevention* (New York: McGraw-Hill Book Company, Inc., 1959).

chapter 2

PRINCIPAL FIRE CHARACTERISTICS

This chapter deals with the thermal decomposition (pyrolysis) of combustibles with the principal emphasis on wood. Closely related are the heat energy and exposure temperatures required to bring about generation of decomposition gases in a sufficient concentration to permit ignition and flaming. The factors which influence and which are involved in flame spread are also discussed, with special attention given to wood structural members and insulated steel deck roofs.

Ignition

Whether ignition of a combustible comes originally from static or other electrical sparks, overheated bearings, cigarettes or matches, spontaneous heating, or from any other source, the ignition itself requires a supply of heat only sufficient to raise the combustible locally to its fire point. The greater the mass of combustible so heated, the finer its state of division, and the better the combustible is arranged for a barely adequate air supply, the lower will be the required temperature and total heat needed from the ignition source. At one end of the scale in ignition resistance would be a solid isolated heavy wood timber and at the other end a flammable vapor or gas already premixed with air.

The initial or primary ignition quite often involves only a very small area or volume of the combustible material. In order to involve additional area, a secondary ignition must come from the heat developed from the primary area of combustion or from a combination of the primary area heat plus some heat from the original ignition source.

Since all flaming fires in common combustible materials

16

are reactions between the oxygen of the atmosphere and gaseous products of vaporization or decomposition, a critical figure for ignition is the temperature required to produce gases or vapors in sufficient concentration to allow the initiation of a flame. While these temperatures for wood and fuel oil might be 800° and 200°F. respectively, both can be ignited by a strong electric spark when finely powdered or atomized and mixed with air at normal temperatures. However, in these cases the spark heats the mixture locally to the ignition temperature and the heat from this very localized combustion raises the temperature of the surrounding mixture so that a spreading flame develops.

On account of the widespread use of wood for structures and furniture, and because many other materials act in a somewhat similar manner, it is appropriate to consider in detail the ignition process of ordinary wood. Unlike flammable liquids and gases, the ignition and combustion of wood is a very complex process.

Ignition of Wood

Wood does not directly unite in combustion with oxygen in its original chemical form. It first passes through a vaporization phase. Upon application of sufficient heat the wood undergoes a process of thermal decomposition, or pyrolysis, to produce a mixture of water vapor, carbon dioxide, combustible gases, and, under rapid heating, a fog of liquid and tarry particles. These products, if mixed in high enough concentration with air, can be ignited by a spark or flame, and, if generated at a high enough rate, are capable of continuous flaming.

If heat is applied at such a low rate that the wood surface does not reach a temperature of about 650°F. or more, decomposition takes place at too slow a rate to produce combustible vapor-air mixtures which can be ignited by a pilot flame. The wood gradually loses its constituents capable of vaporization, it turns darker in color, it slowly becomes charred, and finally consists only of charcoal, residuals of tarry products, and mineral ash. While not capable of flaming combustion, this freshly-formed char material is susceptible to spontaneous heating and to a glowing type of combustion, especially at temperatures above the 300° to 400°F. range if there is a considerable mass of the charred material and other conditions are such as to retain heat.

Up to a temperature slightly above 500°F. the pyrolysis of wood requires the addition of heat, or, in other words, the reaction is endothermic. In the presence of air, however, the products of the pyrolysis will oxidize at temperatures well below 500°F. so that the overall result may be an exothermic or heat producing reaction, but with no danger of fire except under conditions of prolonged exposure favorable to heat retention. For conditions of rapid heating (ignition within 20 minutes) there is some difference in the conclusions of various investigators. Temperatures for ignition of a fresh surface of sound wood are given all the way from about 400°F. to about 840°F. Most of the recent investigators, however, give temperatures for spontaneous ignition in the range of from 662° to 842°F.

Air Temperatures Required for Ignition

During World War II in connection with a study of the ignition effect of incendiaries, a series of experiments was run to determine what air temperatures would be required in order to ignite and induce fire spread over a wood surface under conditions where the heat would be supplied by convection from a nearby localized exposure fire. The wood samples were pieces of Douglas fir, 2 inches wide by 6 inches long by ¾ inch thick, with a moisture content of 8 per cent. A gas burner was used for the heat source, and the arrangement was such as to minimize heating by radiation. The oxygen content was permitted to vary, as might be expected, with a decreasing oxygen percentage in the higher exposure temperature ranges, running about 19 to 20 per cent at temperatures approximating 700°F. down to about 14 to 15 per cent at temperatures between 1,000° and 1,100°F.

Tests were conducted to determine air temperatures required for spontaneous ignition and also for ignition by means of a very small pilot gas flame flicked over the wood surface at intervals of about 5 seconds. With the pilot flame, the wood could be ignited from the mixture of air and products of combustion at about 700°F. in slightly less than 3 minutes from the time the gas burner was ignited. To ignite within 1 minute, temperatures just above 900°F. were needed. Spontaneous ignition, however, required 1,130°F. at 1 minute exposure, and could not be obtained below 1,080°F. regardless of the duration of exposure. Lower temperatures would no doubt have sufficed in both cases had there been a normal oxygen content.

Attempts have been made by some investigators to calculate the actual temperature of the wood surface at the time of ignition by using imbedded thermocouples and figuring the surface temperatures from the thermal conductivity of the wood. This method has a discouraging aspect because of the change in thermal conductivity over the period required to determine minimum ignition temperatures. For example, a fresh sound piece of maple may have a thermal conductivity (across the grain) of roughly 1.00 British thermal unit per square foot per hour per degree F. for a 1-inch thickness. Charcoal from the same piece of wood would probably have a thermal conductivity of 0.35 or less. What the conditions would be in a surface layer of wood undergoing relatively rapid pyrolysis are not known except that the conductivity would undoubtedly be considerably less than 1.00 at the time of ignition.

Heat Energy Required for Ignition

Investigations have been made to determine how much heat energy and at what rate the energy must be applied in order to obtain flaming ignition of wood. In the experiments the heat was applied by radiation from electrically heated elements onto small, smooth, flat pieces or in electric furnaces onto small wafer-like or cylindrical pieces of wood. One of the most notable of these investigations was reported by Lawson and Simms* in 1952. They found that the minimum irradiation for spontaneous ignition of solid wood for most species tested was approximately 0.61 calories per square centimeter per second (about 135 btu per square foot per minute). Ignition in the presence of a pilot flame could be obtained at a heating rate of only about half as much. The higher the radiation heating rate the shorter the ignition time both for spontaneous and pilot ignition. Furthermore, the total required energy of radiation decreases as the time for ignition decreases, presumably because there is a lesser loss of heat mostly from conduction to wood below the surface.

Pyrolysis of Wood

At surface temperatures below about 400°F. the gaseous products of pyrolysis are noncombustible consisting principally of water vapor. From about 400°F. to about 536°F. the gases are still largely noncombustible but contain, in addition to water vapor, carbon dioxide, formic and acetic acids, glyoxal, and traces of carbon monoxide. Above 536°F. the pyrolysis becomes exothermic, and the gases produced contain larger proportions of combustibles including carbon monoxide, methane, methanol, formaldehyde, formic and acetic acids, and later (above 900°F.) consist mostly of hydrogen and carbon monoxide. These gases under conditions of rapid heating of the wood carry with them particles or droplets of highly flammable tars appearing as smoke. Even below 536°F. with very slow heating or with sustained temperatures, oxidation of the products of pyrolysis will occur in the presence of air so that the overall reaction may become exothermic. However, under conditions of rapid heating and pyrolysis which would be needed for spread of flame over a wood surface, the rate of gas evolution prevents access of air to the wood surface. Under these conditions it is concluded that spontaneous ignition

---

*D. I. Lawson and D. L. Simms, "The Ignition of Wood by Radiation," (*British Journal of Applied Physics*, Vol. 3, September 1952, pp. 288-292).

of gases is due to rapid oxidation of the highly combustible tars at temperatures approximating 800°F. although ignition may be obtained from a pilot flame at 700°F. or less.*

Total Developed Heat

As a general rule, damage in a fire is directly related to the total heat developed (the product of the fire intensity in British thermal units per unit area), the extent of the area involved, and the fire duration. It is also closely governed by the available fuel supply — often referred to as "the fire loading." When both the total fire intensity and the duration of fire are substantial, serious damage to buildings and their contents can be expected. However, if either intensity or duration is very low, it is quite possible that the actual damage will be limited to the fuel involved with a rather minor loss. For example, 1 or 2 gallons of gasoline could be spilled on a floor and ignited immediately in a room of large area with a wood plank roof 20 feet above the floor but with a practically noncombustible occupancy except for the gasoline. In such a case there would be an intense fire for a few seconds, but no likely damage except for the loss of the gasoline. On the other hand, we might have eight or ten bales of cotton each weighing several hundred pounds on the floor in the same building. A fire would quickly burn the fuzz from the exterior surfaces of the bales after which the rate of heat production would be rather slow, even though the total heat finally produced might be considerable. Again, there would probably be no damage except to the cotton because of the low fire intensity.

Flame or Fire Spread

Flame spread per se is most important as a communicant of ignition. As the flame spreads, heat is produced at an increasing rate, but in order for the flame to continue to

---

*Note: The reader is referred to the report "Theories of the Combustion of Wood and Its Control" by F. L. Browne, Report No. 2136 (December 1958), the Forest Products Laboratory, U. S. Department of Agriculture, Madison 5, Wisconsin.

spread, the heat developed from the combustion of the involved area must be sufficient to remain in excess of heat losses by conduction, convection, and radiation.

In the usual fire involving common combustible materials, the combustion is an oxidation reaction in which the fuel in the vapor or gas phase combines with oxygen from the air. Thus to obtain a continuing flame, it is necessary that the fuel be present originally in the gaseous form or that sufficient heat be supplied to the fuel to produce combustible vapors in concentrations within the limits of flammability when mixed with air. It is further necessary that the vapor-air mixture be generated at a rate to provide a mixture velocity greater than the lower limit of flame propagation for the fuel involved. If the rate of vapor-air mixture generation is below this limit, the addition of an ignition source may result in a flash but no continuing flame. Ordinarily flames are visible because of the presence of incandescent carbon or of elements such as sodium. If the fuel gases consist primarily of hydrogen and carbon monoxide, the flame may be invisible or nearly so.

The products of combustion from a fire at any stage are hot gases which will rise if they can. These heated gases preheat unburned material above the original fire location and thus tend to spread the fire upwards. At the same time air required for combustion is drawn into the fire from low levels, and this movement of relatively cool air, at least in some degree, prevents or delays progress of the fire downward or laterally in a countercurrent direction. An exception to vertical flame spread occurs when the fire is initiated under a ceiling or roof. In this case the fire must spread laterally unless the roof has a decided slope. Situations where fire spreads laterally over building contents at a substantial rate as compared to the vertical spread are very much in the minority and not too difficult to recognize. Typical situations of this kind may involve storage of textile fibers in bales with fuzzy exterior surfaces, exposed cotton in opener rooms, and storage of cloth or other stock under cutting tables or on multi-tiered solid shelving with-

Factory Mutual Engineering Division

Figure 1. A fire test showing the slow lateral progress of a fire in a wooden crib but the rapid lateral spread under a combustible ceiling.

out lateral subdivision. In each case the fire intensity per unit room area may be relatively low so that the upward travel of hot gases to the ceiling may not allow prompt operation of sprinklers directly over the point where the fire started. Fires which can develop to greater intensity and still travel laterally at high rates can occur in accumulations of loose paper or the trimmings from rolls of plastic film, in heated dryers for festooned cloth or paper, or in exposed spillage of flammable liquids.

There is a type of fire which can persist or spread without any evidence of flame, at least of appreciable length. It is sometimes evidenced by a visible glow but always by the heat generated. This type of fire is fairly common in bales of textile fibers, especially cotton, and may occur in accumulations of powdered metals, organic powders or dusts, soft coal and peat, and in various types of insulation of organic or vegetable origin including cork. It occurs following the flaming stage after decomposition and vaporization have driven off the more volatile constituents. In every case the fuel has a high ratio of surface area to volume, there is little or no volatile fuel being generated, and the porous nature and mass of the material involved tend to retain in some substantial measure the heat of combustion. In its most familiar form, it occurs following flaming fire in ordinary wood, but unlike the flaming stage, the glowing fire in the residual charcoal cannot be discouraged merely by cooling the surroundings. It is necessary to cool the fuel almost down to normal temperatures or to exclude oxygen almost entirely. The cooling can be done generally only by direct wetting, because under most ordinary circumstances the exclusion of oxygen is impracticable. When a fire occurs inside of a cotton bale, which is not readily wetted, the usual procedure is to tear the bale apart so that the pieces can be thoroughly wetted.

Because of the heat retention qualities, a fire in a bale of textile fibers or other large masses of porous materials will persist and spread, but a glowing fire on an exposed wood surface will die out when the exposure is removed. However, a glowing fire in charred wood in the concealed spaces of hollow partitions will persist and spread because heat losses from convection and radiation are much reduced. Fire may also spread in relatively thick combustible insulation even though one surface is exposed to the atmosphere.

Wood Structures

Spread of flame over wood structural members of a building introduces factors which substantially modify any conclusions we might reach, based solely on small scale laboratory experiments, as to temperatures needed for ignition and active flaming combustion. To begin with, except for the immediate area of the usually very much localized ignition, the oxygen content in the ambient atmosphere is reduced by dilution with water vapor and carbon dioxide from the exposing fire. Furthermore, structural members are of substantial thickness and are practically always so arranged that there is almost the maximum opportunity for heat loss by radiation to the relatively cool floor or to building contents at the side or below. Even in the case of light joisted construction where the exposed wood surface subject to combustion is almost twice as much as in a flat, smooth wood ceiling, there is still little interference with heat loss by radiation. In the early stages of a potentially spreading fire over a wood ceiling radiation loss is one of the most important factors. On the other hand, the hot products of combustion from a localized fire in a wood ceiling tend to stay close to the ceiling while they spread out from their point of origin and are quite efficient in heating adjacent areas by the processes of convection and conduction. But as these products of combustion accumulate and raise the temperature of the ceiling not yet involved in flame, they at the same time reduce the oxygen content of the air supply with which they mix so that higher temperatures are required for active combustion of the gases evolved from the wood.

A considerable number of large scale fire tests involving wood ceilings, both smooth and joisted, have shown that a fire will not spread from a locally ignited area unless the area involved is substantial or additional heat is supplied from a strong continuing exposure fire. In order for flame to spread over a wood ceiling or any other wood surface, it is necessary that the heat output from the burning area exceed all heat losses by an amount sufficient to raise the uninvolved perimeter zone to its fire point and to a level required to produce continuous burning. For any given exposure the net heat output (heat produced minus heat losses) can be measured in an apparatus such as the construction materials calorimeter developed in the laboratories of the Factory Mutual Engineering Division. Heat losses can be calculated for any known set of conditions. However, the required heat input for continuous evolution of combus-

Figure 2. The Factory Mutual construction materials calorimeter from the firing end. The construction sample to be tested is shown suspended by chains ready for lowering into place.

tible gases from wood involves a complexity of factors which undergo constant change so that even an approximate calculation is most difficult.

Consider first only a very thin surface layer of smooth, sound wood; heat must be supplied to raise the temperature of the layer through the various stages of decomposition (including heats of decomposition and vaporization) to make up for heat loss by conduction to the wood underneath the layer and to make up for heat loss by radiation which increases with the fourth power of the absolute temperature of the surface. In order to supply this required heat for initial flame spread over a fresh surface of common wood, air temperatures close to the wood surface must be in the range of 700° to 800°F. with air of normal oxygen content. As the oxygen is decreased by dilution with products of combustion, progressively higher temperatures up to

1,000°F. or even more may be needed. As the wood surface changes color during its decomposition, the radiation loss is further increased as the radiation emissivity coefficient changes from its normal value of about 0.9 for sound wood up to 1.0 for a blackened or charred surface. Heat loss by conduction to the air is not a factor when wood is ignited due to the temperature of the atmosphere in contact with it. In the early stages of fire spread over a ceiling, the heat is supplied largely by conduction. Heat supplied by radiation is a minor factor except in areas close to the original igniting exposure. Of course, radiation heat supply becomes a more important factor if the exposure is from a large fire either in ordinary combustibles or in flammable liquids. After the flame spreads initially over the exterior surface layer, the flaming will cease unless temperatures are further increased to compensate for other factors.

Following pyrolysis and evolution of combustible gases from the surface layer, additional combustible gases must come from beneath the surface layer if the flaming is to continue. After the initial surface burning, the surface layer has changed in its physical characteristics and those elements of its composition which can be decomposed or vaporized are much reduced or even eliminated. The charred surface layer acts as a more effective insulator, slowing down the rate of heat transfer from the atmosphere to fresh material in the interior. As the surface layer becomes charred to progressively greater depth the temperature of the exterior must be correspondingly higher in order to transfer the heat through the insulating char to decompose fresh material underneath.

To give some idea how important this insulating effect is we might make the following assumptions: (1) from the work of Lawson and Simms the required heat input for flaming with pilot ignition is 80 btu per square foot per minute, (2) the heat conductivity of sound wood is about 1.0 btu per square foot per hour per °F. for a 1-inch thickness; and is about 0.36 for charcoal. Let us assume that in a surface layer depleted in volatiles the conductivity has been lowered to 0.5. Now if we have a charred surface layer of 1/16 inch thickness with a conductivity of 0.5, we would find by calculation that the exterior would have to be raised 300°F. to get the same heat transfer, so that if 700°F. on the exterior is sufficient for fresh wood, 1,000°F. would be needed after the charring process. If the charred layer should be ⅛ inch thick, the exterior temperature would have to be 1,300°F. There is no point in carrying this any further because after the char has reached a depth of ⅛ inch the surface begins to crack open. It is entirely possible that some heat may be contributed by oxidation of the charred layer, but this is unlikely, because with heating rapid enough to allow continuous flaming, the evolution of unburned fuel gases from the wood would prevent contact between oxygen from the air and the fresh char.

In the progress of a spreading fire over a wood ceiling surface, radiation loss to surroundings is a most important factor, particularly at the high surface temperatures needed to sustain vigorous pyrolysis below the wood surface. On the other hand, radiation back to the surface from the relatively cool diffusion flames from the gaseous products of pyrolysis is not very effective, considering that these gases contain substantial proportions of noncombustible elements and are mixed with air having a below normal oxygen content. The most important heat supply to the wood surface is by the process of conduction from the layer of hot products of combustion under the ceiling. In a large area these hot combustion products flow away from involved zones and mix with cooler air from below, at the same time dropping further in temperature on account of conduction to adjacent surfaces. Consequently, unless temperatures are maintained ahead of the flaming area by heat from a substantial continuing exposure or the burning area is quite large, the loss of heat by radiation from the wood surface will exceed any gain which is primarily by conduction from hot combustion products, and the flaming will die out.

This course of events has been demonstrated many times in actual large scale fire tests. As an example, one fire was initiated in a ceiling of fir planking (moisture content about 14 per cent) in a test structure 20 feet wide by 100 feet long and with a head room of 10 feet. An exposure fire was supplied sufficient in size to heat the first 20 feet of length at the ceiling at a rate in accordance with the standard ASTM time-temperature curve for testing fire resistance. When the wood ceiling had become ignited and involved in active flaming for a distance of 40 feet (about 800 square feet), the exposure fire was abruptly cut off. Even though flaming continued for 2 or 3 minutes and extended to about 60 feet, the heat losses were greater than the supply from the combustion so that flaming died out at about 10 minutes after the beginning of the test. There were only a few flickering flames and some glowing combustion left in the zone first directly exposed.

The preceding discussion and the example cited should be kept in mind when we later consider sprinkler protection and the necessity of stressing control and extinguishment of fire in building occupancy, with protection of the ceiling having a less important role.

Factory Mutual Engineering Division

Figure 3. Roof deck test structure ready for fire test.

Insulated Steel Deck Roofs

Several years ago following a disastrous fire in an automotive parts manufacturing plant, there was a great deal of interest in assessing the fire hazard and flame spread characteristics of insulated steel deck roofs, particularly those in which the wood fiber insulation was bonded to the steel deck by asphalt, sometimes in two coats with a layer of asphalt-impregnated roofing felt between. The amount of asphalt ran from about 12 to 15 pounds for each 100 square feet for the single coat to about 28 pounds per 100 square feet for the double coat.

When a layer of steel is interposed between an exposing fire and a combustible as in an insulated steel deck roof, the rate of heat transfer from the fire into the combustible is slowed down. In the first place, the temperature of the steel must be raised to a point where it can in turn transfer heat to the combustible above at a sufficient rate to produce continuously the required concentration for flaming of fuel gases which issue from the combustible and pass through the joints in the steel decking. In addition, the steel, even after being raised to the required temperature, offers some resistance to the flow of heat through the steel even though it is a relatively poor insulator. For any required temperature above the steel deck, the temperature below must be higher in order to effect the needed transfer of heat to the fuel above.

Since the asphalt which is used as an adhesive to fasten the wood fiber insulation to the steel is in direct contact with the latter, the asphalt is in the best position to absorb heat from the steel. Therefore, if fire conditions below are severe enough, flaming underneath the steel deck is first produced by distillation products from the asphalt seeping through the deck joints, and then later by decomposition and vaporization of combustible gases from the fiber above. The steel deck, however, does have a beneficial effect in serving as a mechanical support for the insulation above, preventing it from falling on account of delamination which would produce a more hazardous condition. In addition, it helps in some respect to reduce the tendency of the asphalt to fall in burning drops, which would probably ignite any combustibles on the floor, particularly when the asphalt is applied by narrow strip mopping (about 8 to 10 pounds per 100 square feet). With greater amounts of asphalt, some burning drip is almost inevitable in spite of the steel deck.

The action discussed in the preceding paragraph is illustrated in Figure 4 which shows the results of a series of tests involving three types of roof coverings. The tests were conducted in the Factory Mutual construction materials calorimeter and were run at the relatively severe "standard" exposure adopted for this equipment. Referring to Curves "A" and "B" in Figure 4, it will be noted that the sharp rise in heat output occurred about 2 minutes later for the steel deck protected insulation than for the bare wood planking. This is due to the heat required to raise the steel

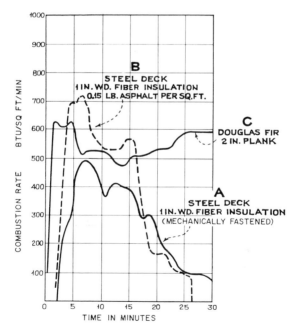

Figure 4. Examples of construction materials calorimeter test results.

to the temperature necessary for the proper heat transfer and also because of the small insulation effect of the steel deck. Because of the greater flammability of the asphalt and its close contact with the steel, the sharp rise to maximum heat output took place almost 2 minutes ahead of the sample with no asphalt, and the actual heat output was about 200 btu per square foot per minute greater. The very substantial heat output (above 300 btu per square foot per minute) lasted about 15 minutes with the asphalt and about 13 minutes with the fiber insulation alone. After these times the heat production fell off quite rapidly as the insulation burned out.

Curve "C" in Figure 4, illustrating the results of the test with exposed 2-inch thick Douglas fir plank, shows the early sharp rise to maximum heat output without the protective influence of the steel deck. It also shows the greater maximum output of bare wood as compared to the insulated steel deck without the asphalt mopping. Furthermore, on account of the larger weight of fuel available, the heat produced from the bare wood averages above 500 btu per square foot per minute for the whole duration of the ½-hour test.

Several tests have been made in large scale in a 100-foot long test structure using 1-inch thick wood fiber insulation mechanically fastened to the steel deck (no asphalt mopping). In these tests with an exposure to equal the effect of the standard time-temperature test curve (NFPA No. 251, Standard Methods of Fire Tests of Building Construction and Materials) for the first 20 feet of the test structure, flame did not spread the entire length of the structure. Following these tests and many others on various roof combinations, it was decided that the fire spread hazard of the insulated deck with no asphalt adhesive was sufficiently low so that sprinkler protection might be omitted provided that the occupancy of the building was without enough fire hazard to call for sprinkler protection. While this decision was based on wood fiber insulation mechanically fastened to the steel deck, acceptability without sprinklers was naturally extended to any combination which after adequate testing showed equal or lesser flame spread hazard, and where an excellent performance on the part of both manufacturer and installer of the roofing could be relied on.

Since any type of construction which can liberate over 400 btu per square foot per minute for a period of 10 minutes is far from noncombustible, the decision was a matter of underwriting judgment. It must have been presumed that there would be no major changes in occupancy hazard without adequate warning and that inspectors would be competent to recognize degrees of occupancy hazard. In this latter respect tests have shown that the exposure used in the large scale roof deck tests was no greater than could be expected from a row of 8-foot high stacks of 4-foot square slatted hardwood pallets, and with only two or three stacks in the row. However, this matter of recognition of hazards requiring sprinklers is no different for these cases than it would be for any type of roof with little or no combustibility.

chapter 3

FIRE INTENSITY

A fire can be quite small and still be very intense in the sense of liberating a great deal of heat per unit area or per unit volume; an example is the acetylene torch. However, the term fire intensity is commonly used to include both the rate of heat release per unit of area and the area involved, or the total rate of heat release from the fire regardless of the fire area. Since all flaming fires involve three dimensions, it would be more proper to express fire intensity in terms of British thermal units per unit volume, but for general fire protection purposes it is more convenient to think of fire intensity in British thermal units per square foot of floor area.

Fire intensity depends not only on the characteristics and properties of the combustible, but more importantly on the physical state and arrangement of the fuel, the surrounding temperature conditions, and on many other factors, none of which can be ignored. As a result we may have fires in materials which are not ordinarily considered to be highly combustible but because of special conditions of arrangement are more intense in terms of British thermal units per unit floor area than are fires in some of the volatile flammable liquids. As an example, a fire in a single 8-foot high stack of moderately dry hardwood slatted pallets will liberate about 10 per cent more heat than a gasoline fire of the same 16-square-foot area at the maximum intensity for both. This assumes burning in a spacious area with no external radiated heat.

In the following paragraphs an attempt will be made to discuss the most important factors which might be involved in a determination of fire intensity in ordinary combustible materials.

Factory Mutual Engineering Division

Figure 5. Fire almost fully developed in 8-foot-high stack of hardwood pallets.

Physical State and Arrangement

As a fuel material is increasingly reduced in cross section — as is wood all the way from heavy timbers down through planks, boards, small pieces used for kindling, shavings, sawdust, and finally wood flour — it becomes more easy to ignite. This is because it takes less heat to bring a small section up to the ignition temperature and because the greater surface area relative to mass (specific surface) allows a more efficient transfer of heat from the igniting exposure. It does not follow, however, that an increased fire intensity results from fine subdivision alone. For example, a mass of wood flour burns relatively slowly because the access of air to all surfaces except on the exterior is very much impeded as is also the escape of products of combustion. On the other hand, if these impediments are largely removed by suspending the flour in the atmosphere, burning may take place so fast as to cause an explosion under some degree of confinement.

Common examples of materials with high specific surface are vegetable insulating board, baled cotton fiber, and wood charcoal. In each case ignition requires only a small amount of heat energy, and because porous materials are naturally good thermal insulators, a large proportion of combustion heat is retained in the material so that fire progress is quite persistent through a mass of the material even though the fire intensity may be relatively low.

Another example of a material with a very high specific surface, but in which the physical arrangement affects the ease of ignition, is the highly compressed Egyptian cotton bale (about 35 pounds per cubic foot). In this case the insulating value is reduced and the air supply between the fibers is so much decreased that ignition *inside* such a bale, whether by spontaneous heating or by any other means, is practically impossible. In the case of soft cotton bales (20 to 24 pounds per cubic foot) there is more space between the fibers, and air can diffuse into and through the bale so that a glowing fire can persist and spread.

Air Supply

In order to bring about ignition of common combustibles, oxygen for the reaction must be available, and for the resultant fire to spread and grow in intensity, an ever increasing air and oxygen supply is required. While close spacing of combustibles in a pile makes it easier to start a fire, close spacing also impedes the inflow of air to the interior of the pile so that the fire intensity (heat produced per unit floor area) may be very much limited. What usually happens in such a case is that the fire in the pile develops to a degree of intensity above which heat is produced within the pile at a rate sufficient to decompose and vaporize more fuel than can be burned within the pile. The resultant fuel gases then issue from the upper zones of the pile and mix with the more readily available air above the pile. The mixture burns in flames, the length of the flames governed by the rate at which the unburned fuel gases are produced.

When ordinary combustibles including wood, cotton, vegetable, and mineral oils and their byproducts are oxidized, the heat produced is directly governed by the oxygen consumed in the reaction. For practically all compounds of carbon and hydrogen, or carbon, hydrogen, and oxygen, the heat produced in the combustion is very close to 500 btu per cubic foot of oxygen consumed or 105 btu per cubic foot of air, both calculated at 70°F. What this means is that for almost all ordinary combustibles the air supply to the fire is the limiting factor regardless of the quantity, nature, and arrangement of the combustible. Hydrogen, carbon, carbon monoxide, and compounds containing nitrogen or sulphur do not follow this rule.

An interesting illustration of the effect of restricting air supply was given in a description of comparative tests using a pair of spaced wood panels 4 feet wide by 8 feet high with the sides closed but with the tops and bottoms open. The spacing of the opposed parallel panels in one case was $1\frac{1}{4}$ inches and in another $7\frac{1}{4}$ inches. The maximum heat liberation rate for the fire in the close-spaced panels was less than 20 per cent of the rate with the wide-spaced panels, the latter having less restriction on air access and escape of combustion products.*

In order for any fire to reach maximum intensity and to continue at a high rate, the air supply to the whole fire

---

*N. J. Thompson, "Hazard of High Piled Stock," NFPA *Quarterly,* July 1949, pp. 38-46.

including any generated fuel gases must be maintained, and there must be some facility for adequate exhaust of the products of combustion. These conditions are met when the fire is out of doors, and to a large degree when the fire is in a building of large area with generous headroom. In small rooms or even in fairly large rooms with only a few feet of clearance between the floor and ceiling, the magnitude of the fire may be restricted in the absence of large sized air intake and exhaust openings. Under such conditions, the products of combustion build up first at high levels after which they travel downward so that sooner or later the atmosphere reaching the fire is mixed with products of combustion; thus the air supply to the fire is diluted, with a continuing reduction in its oxygen content. In practice, unfortunately, practically all building structures admit enough air by leakage and diffusion so that temperatures will stay at high and damaging levels. Consequently, no complete fire extinguishment by this means can be expected. However, with automatic sprinkler protection, the movement of the products of combustion down into the zone around the fire is accelerated with a correspondingly increased oxygen deficiency in this zone. The resultant effect in reducing the fire intensity is no small factor in the effectiveness of sprinklers, particularly in areas of low to moderate headroom. It is especially noticeable for fires in volatile flammable liquids which are immune to the cooling effect of water. The author recalls at least one instance of a test fire in sprayed gasoline in a large area with a ceiling height of 16 feet in which the fire was completely extinguished by the action of sprinklers on ordinary spacing and at only 24 pounds per square inch water pressure.

Effect of Temperature

For ordinary combustibles, such as wood, the temperature of the exposing atmosphere is usually the most important factor in fire intensity and rapidity of spread. Except for the original locus of ignition, fire spread is almost always caused by the heated combustion products from the area already burning. Thus fire tends to spread upward in piles of combustible materials or horizontally under a combustible ceiling. As the exposure temperature increases, whether accompanied by radiated heat or not, there is a greater rate of decomposition and production of combustible gases. However, for a combustible surface such as wood this may not be strictly true except for the production of combustible gases at or close to the surface. As these are evolved the residual charred material depleted in volatile constituents acts as an insulator to the passage of heat to the interior so that an even higher exposure may be needed just to maintain the same fire intensity.

Tests have been run in a construction materials calorimeter at the laboratories of the Factory Mutual Engineering Division to determine the rates of heat evolution from a wood plank ceiling under conditions of relatively severe exposure.* With the standard exposure for this apparatus (reaching about 1,400°F. in a minute and 1,600°F. in 5 minutes) the Douglas fir samples burned to produce a little over 600 btu per square foot per minute for a period of 4 minutes following the first 1½ minutes of exposure, after which it dropped to a little over 500 btu per square foot per minute even though the exposure temperature had increased to about 1,650°F. When a fresh sample of fir wood was put in the calorimeter the rate of heat input through the exposing burners was reduced by about 30 per cent. The maximum heat contribution from the sample was only about 430 btu per square foot per minute occurring for a short period from 1½ to 3½ minutes from the start of the test. On the other hand, increasing the exposure burner fuel rate by only about 14 per cent resulted in a maximum heat contribution from the sample of almost 900 btu per square foot per minute. From these results it is obvious that under favorable conditions for the buildup and transfer of heat, fires in materials of moderate combusti-

*N. J. Thompson, E. W. Cousins, "The FM Construction Materials Calorimeter," NFPA *Quarterly,* January 1959, pp. 186-192.

bility can develop to fairly high intensities and spread quite rapidly.

Oxygen Deficient Atmospheres

The fuel gases from the pyrolysis of common species of wood will oxidize rapidly when mixed with normal air at temperatures around the order of 500°F., but in order to burn with a continuous flame, the air temperatures must be about 800°F. or be brought to this level by some ignition source. Of course, after ignition has been obtained, the heat of the combustion quickly raises temperatures to higher levels. If the oxygen content of the atmosphere is reduced below normal, higher fuel gas-air mixture temperatures are needed in order to initiate and sustain flaming. When the oxygen content is reduced to the general order of 8 per cent or less, no visible flaming can be observed even at mixture temperatures as high as 1,500°F. However, oxidation of the fuel gases still continues although at a much lower rate per unit volume of the mixture than with higher oxygen concentration.

Some years ago a series of laboratory experiments were performed in which wood (dry Douglas fir) was heated in the absence of air to produce combustible fuel gases. These gases were then mixed with heated air at several decreasing oxygen contents and at various temperatures. It was found that oxidation still continued as long as the air had any oxygen content, and that the rate of oxidation increased as the temperature was increased in the range tested (above 1,000°F.). The oxidation took place in a long ceramic tube, and temperature observation throughout the length of the tube showed that the zone of active oxidation (heat production) lengthened as the oxygen proportion decreased. These experiments assist in explaining what happened in some large scale tests of wooden roofs in which, after initial charring, temperatures continued to rise even with no visible glowing or flaming. Temperatures were in the range of from 1,200° to 1,500°F.

in the layer of gases below the roof while the oxygen content of the layer varied from 4 to 7 per cent. Since, after the initial charring, the decomposition gases from the wood carried no tars or carbon particles, the combustion flames were nonluminous and thus not visible.

An example of the effect of reduced oxygen content is to be found in fire tests involving joisted roof construction fire-stopped at distances of 20 feet. On account of the lowered oxygen content due to confinement of the products of combustion, active flaming ceased and the combustion rate of the wood was very markedly reduced even under identical conditions of exposure as compared to continuous open joists in which the oxygen deficient atmosphere was not prevented from flowing away from the exposed location.

Effect of Height of Combustibles

Articles made of wood, paper, and many other substances are capable of being piled to considerable heights. Since the hot products of combustion in a fire initiated at the bottom or low levels in piled goods tend to rise, the combustion heat is transferred by convection and conduction to surfaces above the original fire location. Thus the growth of fire vertically takes place at a rapid rate unless there are effective barriers to the upward movement of hot gases. If the vertical spaces in the pile are restricted, the hot gases of combustion will be forced into more horizontal paths, tending to promote lateral fire spread. Spread of fire in a downward direction is usually very slow indeed, not only because hot gases tend to rise, but also because of the cooling effect of entering fresh air coming mostly from below to feed the fire. In general, spread of fire downward is due primarily to ignition by radiation from a hot, well-established fire.

The effect of increasing combustible height while holding other dimensions constant was shown dramatically in the experiments previously mentioned.* The parallel op-

*See page 37; also "Hazards of High Piled Stock," NFPA *Quarterly*, July 1949, pp. 38-46.

posed spruce board panels were spaced 8 inches apart and the ignition was from a fairly strong source, a small wad of cellucotton soaked with gasoline. In the test series four panels, 4, 8, 12, and 16 feet high, were used. Since the tests were conducted in a large room with a 33-foot high ceiling, there was an entirely adequate air supply in every test. The fire intensities were roughly measured by burning gasoline in the form of a spray at rates to produce the same average ceiling temperatures. From these measurements the maximum fire intensities in terms of heat produced were judged to vary in the ratios of 1.0, 2.4, 6.8, and 22.0 for the heights of 4, 8, 12, and 16 feet respectively.

Effect of Radiation

According to the Stefan-Boltzman law, heat transferred by radiation from a hot surface is proportional to the difference between the 4th powers of the absolute temperatures of the radiating surface and its surroundings, with some modification depending on the nature of the surface (its radiation emissivity coefficient) and the shape and relation of the surface to surrounding objects (the configuration factor).* To give some idea how important radiation losses can become with higher surface temperatures, Table 1 shows the approximate calculated radiated heat from a ceiling to a floor or occupancy below the ceiling where the ceiling and floor areas are very large in relation to the distance from floor to ceiling and where the intervening atmosphere is essentially transparent to radiation transmission.

The following illustrates the effect of radiation loss: If the flat surface of a wood board is ignited locally by a small flame, the flame will quickly die out if the exposure is removed. Even if the small flame is maintained, there will be very little spread of fire mostly because of the radiation loss which is relatively large at the temperatures necessary for continuous burning. However, if we have two such wood

---

*Note: For a much more complete discussion of radiant energy the reader is referred to the book *Heat Transmission* by William H. McAdams, McGraw-Hill Book Company, Inc., New York City (1954).

Table 1: Energy Radiated Between Two Parallel Surfaces
Emissivity coefficient = 1.0 (black body)

Temperature at Floor	Radiated Heat Loss to Floor Btu per square foot per minute						
	Ceiling Surface Temperature, °F.						
	800	900	1,000	1,100	1,200	1,300	1,400
100°F.	70	94	123	162	208	263	330
500°F.	49	74	103	141	187	243	310
1,000°F.	—	—	0	39	85	136	203

boards with a small space between, they cannot lose heat by radiation to each other because they are both roughly at the same temperature, and the loss to the surroundings is very substantially reduced so that the fire may spread even after the original small igniting flame has been removed.

A familiar example of a self-sustaining fire is two or more wood logs closely spaced in a fireplace, the separation being only enough to permit the entrance of air for combustion. If the logs are too far apart, an unfavorable configuration factor is introduced, and the radiation loss may be too great for the establishment of a self-sustaining fire. A single log will burn only as long as the kindling exposure is maintained.

Combustion Gases and Radiation

The composition, temperature, and thickness of the gas layer under a wood ceiling can have an important effect on radiation loss (or gain) from (or to) the burning surface. The radiation loss is reduced as the temperature of the gases increases, as the emissivity coefficient increases, and as the thickness of the gas layer increases. If the emissivity, temperature, and thickness reach a sufficient level, heat may be transferred to the ceiling and the exposure increased.

For all practical purposes, the normal atmosphere is transparent to radiation. It consists almost entirely of elemental gases which have no ability to emit or absorb radiation within the temperature range of interest to the fire protection engineer. In addition to nitrogen and oxygen, air contains very small amounts of carbon dioxide (about 0.03 per cent), varying amounts of water vapor from about 0.75 per cent at 70°F. and 30 per cent relative humidity to about 6.5 per cent in a saturated atmosphere at 70°F., slightly less than 1 per cent argon, and traces of neon, helium, krypton, and xenon.

Gases found in combustion products such as carbon dioxide, carbon monoxide, water vapor, sulfur dioxide, alcohols, aldehydes, and ammonia do have sufficient absorptivity to affect transmission of radiant energy, depending on the partial pressures of the individual gases and the thickness of the gas layer. In a gas mixture containing two or more gases, however, the total absorption or emission is not the sum of the individual effects but an amount somewhat less than the sum, since each gas is slightly opaque to the others.

To give an idea of the magnitude of the radiation characteristics of some common combustion products, the following figures show the approximate emissivity or absorptivity at 1,500°F. for a 10 per cent concentration in a gas layer about 1 foot in thickness: Carbon dioxide, 0.076; carbon monoxide, 0.093; water vapor, 0.054; and sulfur dioxide, 0.07. While the emissivity increases with the partial pressure or concentration of the particular gas and with the thickness of the whole gaseous layer, the increase is somewhat less than proportional. Therefore, in order for a nonluminous flame to have any substantial effect on radiation heat loss, the layer would have to be several feet thick, at which time the question of continued flame spread would depend largely on factors other than radiation.

When flame begins to spread over a wood ceiling, for example, tarry compounds are distilled rapidly from the wood surface. These compounds decompose into hydrocarbons and carbon particles which produce a luminous flame. However, the thickness of the flame layer is usually only a few inches so that total radiation emission or absorption by the flame is not of great importance in reducing the radiation loss from the burning wood surface. After the initial flaming, a layer of char is formed on the wood surface that slows down penetration of heat into the interior of the wood. The rate of decomposition of the wood material underneath the char is decreased which in turn decreases the rate of evolution of tarry materials. The concentration of hydrogen and carbon monoxide is increased and the concentration of tarry substances is decreased. The resultant gases, almost free from particles of carbon, oxidize in a mixture with air in a nonluminous flame with a greatly decreased effect on radiation losses from the charred surface, unless the flame layer builds up to a depth of several feet in thickness.

Where there is a continuous exposure to a combustible structure from burning oil, asphalt or gasoline, or from the rapid burning of ordinary combustibles in considerable bulk, the flames are quite luminous since they carry large amounts of carbon or sooty particles from the cracking of tars or gaseous hydrocarbons. Such flames in substantial volume not only increase the exposure to the construction but may prevent any radiation losses from the structure surface. The radiation emissivities from these flames in depths over 3 feet may run as high as 0.6 or even up 0.8 or more. Flames in pulverized coal fired boilers may have emissivities from 0.9 to almost 1.0.

Water Fog and Radiation

The emissivity and absorptivity of a liquid water surface are relatively high, around the order of 0.95. In a natural water fog, however, the ratio of volume of the liquid water to the volume of the air between the drops is quite low so that the fog may be somewhat poor in its ability to absorb radiation if the fog is only a few feet in thickness. On the other hand, natural fogs from 50 feet to several hundred feet in thickness can substantially reduce the radiation from the sun. In fire protection, artificially produced fogs of high density and several feet in thickness have been found to be very helpful in cutting down the transmission of radiant heat so as to protect the manual firefighter. In considering the part that a water fog may play in affecting radiation to or from a combustible structure surface, the zones where the temperature conditions would permit a fog of condensed water vapor to exist are well outside of the regions where active flame spread is involved. Consequently, it is believed that condensation of water vapor in any building fire is of no importance in limiting fire spread. The only major part which water vapor might play in fire spread would be to dilute the oxygen concentration in the atmosphere and in this manner reduce the fire intensity.

Fire Intensity Factors Illustrated

To illustrate the effect on fire intensity of some of the variables explained earlier in this chapter, we refer again to tests in the Factory Mutual construction materials calorimeter and to the tests on opposing parallel panels of varying height.*

In the calorimeter tests the principal variable was the exposure temperature. With samples of Douglas fir, the maximum heat liberated for a 3-minute period was about 400 btu per square foot per minute at an exposure temperature of from 1,200° to 1,250°F. The heat liberation was approximately 600 btu per square foot per minute at an exposure temperature of 1,500°F. In both cases the radiation losses were about normal for the sample temperatures because the floor and sidewalls of the test furnace had not heated substantially during the period in which this data was taken (less than 5 minutes). The air supply in both cases was more than ample so that there was no significant oxygen deficiency.

The tests with the parallel spruce panels are particularly enlightening; they included a few of the most significant variables — reduction in radiation losses on account of the spacing of the panels (only 8 inches apart), an air supply roughly tailored to the combustion needs by natural draft, and the effect of combustible height which serves to raise the exposure temperature above any flaming zone.

*See pages 37 and 41; also "Hazards of High Piled Stock," NFPA *Quarterly*, July 1949, pp. 38-46.

Combustible subdivision was not a factor because, except for height, all samples were the same, and the moisture content was held quite closely between 10 and 12 per cent.

For samples of 8, 12, and 16 feet high respectively, the maximum rates of heat release were judged to be 48,000, 136,000 and 440,000 btu per minute. Based on total interior surface the heat release rates were 670, 1,230, and 3,000 btu per square foot per minute, and based on the projected floor area of the interior (2.67 square feet), the rates of heat release per square foot of floor area were approximately 18,000, 51,000 and 165,000 btu per square foot per minute.

The preceding example shows in a striking manner the tremendous effect on fire intensity due to reduction of radiant heat loss and due to the increase in combustible height when combined with conditions for a favorable air supply. Fortunately, in actual practice, we seldom find all these factors present simultaneously, at least to such a degree. When combustible stock is piled to more than moderate heights, floor space limitations force more compact piling so that combustible surfaces are much closer together restricting the air supply. Moreover, since stock piles are usually fairly substantial in area, ready access of air into the pile except near to the exterior is even more restricted because of the resistance to lateral flow of air exerted by the pile thickness.

One of the familiar examples of favorable conditions for fire intensity is displayed by the ordinary hardwood slatted pallet when stored in high piles. Let us consider an 8-foot-high stack of 4-foot-square pallets with 2-inch by 4-inch longitudinal stringers. The stringers on the outside prevent the ready access of air, except in the small spaces between the floor slats. However, the ends of the pallets are entirely open. With a strong ignition source, a fire in such a pile attains maximum intensity in a little over 5 minutes and then liberates about 360,000 btu per minute. Now if we start a fire in two closely spaced pallet stacks with the open ends together, the maximum rate of heat release is about 600,000 btu per minute, considerably less than twice that from the single stack. While we have the

Factory Mutual Engineering Division

Figure 6. Heavy smoke billows from a test fire in only 450 rubber tires piled 8 feet high on the floor.

same conditions of favorable radiation and stack height, the access of air to the center is restricted by the double length of travel from the open ends to the center.

Another example of factors influencing fire intensity and which received a great deal of attention a few years ago is the piling of automobile tires, especially to heights of over 8 feet. At first, the tires were piled directly on each other on the floor, but later, in order to conserve floor space and to give intermediate support, the tires were piled on wood or steel pallets. However, the fire hazard was governed primarily by the piling height, regardless of the pallets, and required especially strong water supplies for sprinkler protection. In fact, there is still a little doubt about the practicability of sprinkler protection for piles as high as 16 feet.

chapter 4

TRAVEL OF COMBUSTION PRODUCTS

The combustion products of any fire will rise almost vertically if they can, because with their elevated temperature they are lighter than the surrounding atmosphere. The rate of upward travel is roughly proportional to the gas temperature, which in turn depends on the intensity of the fire which produces the gases. An understanding of the travel direction and temperature gradient in combustion products is essential in deciding on the best position of sprinklers so as to obtain prompt operation of the sprinklers, especially in view of the deflecting action of structural elements on the travel of the combustion gases.

Ceiling Temperature Gradients

As the hot products of combustion from a flaming fire rise, air from the surrounding atmosphere mixes with the gases so that the temperature of the mixture decreases. The maximum ceiling temperature from any given fire occurs when the headroom is low, although the ceiling temperature gradient falls off rapidly in zones close to a point directly over the fire and less rapidly at greater distances. When the fire occurs in a room with a high ceiling, the temperature directly over the fire is less than with a low ceiling, and the temperature gradient is decreased. Moreover, the greater the fire intensity the greater the temperature gradient at the ceiling.

This falling off in temperature is illustrated in Figure 7, which shows graphically the results of tests with gasoline pan fires in a room 60 by 80 by 15½ feet high from which combustion gases could finally flow into an adjoining area 40 by 60 by 33 feet high. Gasoline pan areas were 2, 5, 9, and 15 square feet producing about 15,000, 40,000, 80,000, and 150,000 btu per minute respectively. In these

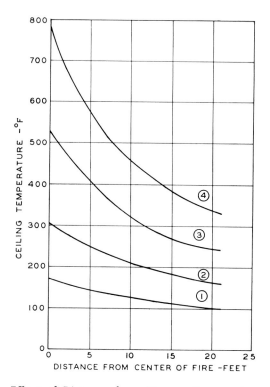

Figure 7. Effect of Distance from Fire on Temperature Gradients

Gasoline pan fire on floor — 15½ feet headroom — temperatures (near maximum) recorded 6 minutes after ignition.

Test No.	Surface Area of Pans (Square Feet)	Approximate Heat (Btu per Min.)
1	2	15,000
2	5	40,000
3	9	80,000
4	15	150,000

tests, all windows, doors, and roof hatches were closed so that the air supply was limited to the volume of the building (roughly 154,000 cubic feet) plus some inevitable leakage. The temperatures shown in Figure 7 are from thermocouples located 8 inches below the smooth plastered ceiling and were recorded about 6 minutes after ignition. The temperatures are near the maximums for the size fire tested. The temperature gradient under the ceiling from a point centered over the fire is clearly shown at various distances in feet. It should be pointed out, however, that these test gasoline fires reached almost maximum intensity in a very short time and thus are not typical of fires in ordinary solid combustibles. Consequently, the temperature gradients for the gasoline fires are more pronounced.

The relatively rapid build-up in intensity in a gasoline

Factory Mutual Engineering Division

Figure 8. Fire in double 8-foot stacks of pallets under a 33-foot-high ceiling.

pan fire test is shown in **Figure 9.** This shows the same data for one of the test fires reported in Figure 7 (5-foot-square pan) but with temperatures recorded at 1, 2, 3, and 5 minutes after ignition. It will be seen by examination of Figure 9 that most of the intensity build-up takes place in the first 2 minutes of the fire.

The differences in maximum temperatures over the fire and in ceiling temperature gradients for rooms of low and high headroom are shown in Figure 10, which gives results of two tests, each involving two adjacent 8-foot-high stacks of 4- by 4-foot hardwood slatted pallets with moisture contents from 12 to 13 per cent. Each double stack weighed approximately 3,300 pounds. The tests were run in the same test building — one test in the center of the low section (4,800 square feet) and the other in the center of the high section (2,400 square feet). In both tests there was an ex-

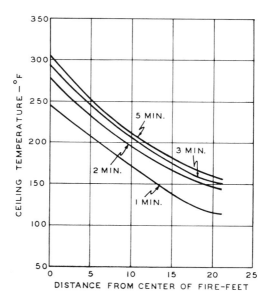

Figure 9. Heat Intensity Gradients

Five-foot-square gasoline pan fire — approximately 40,000 btu per minute heat release — 15½-foot headroom.

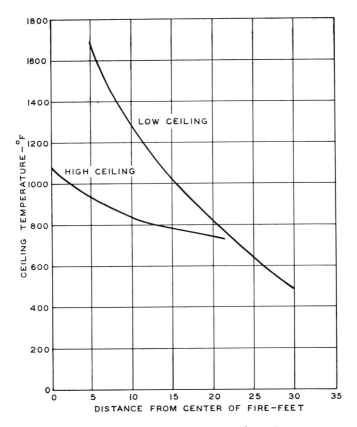

Figure 10. Effect of Headroom on Ceiling Temperatures

Test fires identical 8-foot-high double stacks of wooden pallets — maximum heat release about 600,000 btu per minute — temperatures recorded 15 minutes after ignition — 14-square-foot exhaust vent open in high section of test structure.

haust opening of 14 square feet in the high section. In each case there was a period of 5 minutes or slightly more required for the fires to reach maximum intensity, and the maximum ceiling temperatures occurred at about 17 minutes after ignition. Temperatures shown were those recorded about 15 minutes after the start of the fire at thermocouples located 8 inches below the ceiling.

While Figure 10 shows much higher ceiling temperatures over and within 15 to 20 feet of the fire as well as the steeper temperature gradient for the low ceiling, it will also be noted that the ceiling temperatures for the test with the reduced headroom become lower than those of the high section test at distances over 22 feet laterally from the fire center. This is because the area of the low section was twice that of the high section, thus permitting the products of combustion to spread out more, losing more heat by conduction to the ceiling and by dilution in the greater volume.

The data from these comparative tests on double stacks of pallets are presented in a somewhat different manner in Table 2, which shows how much more uniform the ceiling temperatures are in a building with generous headroom. Furthermore, for this moderately severe fire (about 600,000 btu per minute) in a room with a low ceiling there would be quite a substantial area over which failure of steel roof supports might be expected, whereas with the high ceiling, damage to exposed steel supports would be largely limited to distortion on account of expansion with little or no actual steel collapse.

Table 2: Effect of Headroom on Ceiling Temperatures

Ceiling Temperatures	High Section Height — 33 ft. Area — 2,400 sq. ft.	Low Section Height — 15½ ft. Area — 4,800 sq. ft.
Maximum temperature, average for 20- by 20-ft. area over fire	850°F.	1,470°F.
Average temperature, entire area	800°F.	850°F.
Amount of area above 800°F.	570 sq. ft.	1,450 sq. ft.

Velocity of Combustion Gases

The upward velocity of hot gases from any fire increases with the total fire intensity. This velocity may be hardly discernible from a small smoldering fire and may be only a few feet per second for a small flaming fire. However, in the case of an intense fire, as in high-piled stock with good air access, upward velocities from 10 to 30 feet per second may be expected. In a series of laboratory test fires in which gasoline was burned at the rate of a little less than 10 gallons per minute in a well-vented area, the upward velocity was measured at a point about 15 feet above the burning gasoline spray. The total heat liberation was about 1,115,000 btu per minute and the intensity in the zone of measurement was roughly 10,000 btu per square foot per minute. The upward velocity was found to be 56 feet per second which is equal to 38 miles per hour. The velocity would have been very much less if the upward travel had been impeded by a low ceiling or by lack of adequate exhaust vents.

The hot gases from a fire rise to the ceiling and then, if the ceiling is smooth and unbroken, spread out like water over a level plain. For any localized fire at a stage which would open ordinary sprinklers, the lateral movement of gases from a point directly over the fire is usually around the order of 2 to 10 feet per second at distances within 7 feet. These velocities decrease roughly at somewhat more than the square of the distance at points further removed from the fire.

Influence of Structural Elements

Where the ceiling is subdivided by beams or joists the gases flow in the resulting channels much like water in a river bed. The shallower and narrower the channel, the less the flow rate needed for overflow. In the same fashion hot gases from a fire will flow out under and across joists or beams. The narrower the joist or bay channel, the sooner will this lateral overflow take place. At the same time, the travel of hot gases will always extend further in a direction parallel to the channels than at right angles to them.

Where beams are framed into girders or where bays are subdivided into compartments by fire stopping, the situation can be likened to a river with a dam as high as the river bank, in which water will flow over the bank as soon as the level reaches the top of the dam. In a like manner, combustion gases rising to the compartments or pockets will fill them and then overflow into adjacent compartments. Where a roof is of the saw-tooth variety or is broken up with monitors, each of these spaces acts as a heat reservoir which must be filled before the hot gases can flow on to the next space. Consequently, they serve as valuable time delays in the general spread of high temperatures over the entire roof or ceiling.

If there are open windows in the saw teeth or in the monitors, the action is like a drain in a water basin so that the spread of heat is further delayed, and if the openings are large enough in relation to the rate of development of hot gases, they may stop entirely the spread of high temperatures. The same type of action can be obtained with a flat roof if it is divided into compartments by draft curtains with exhaust vents in each compartment. On the other hand, the provision of vents in a flat roof without draft curtains is of extremely limited value, because the "stack effect," which is necessary to the upward movement of heated air through the vent, is restricted to a relatively thin layer of gases under the roof. By the time this layer of hot gases increases in thickness to the point where there is a well pronounced stack effect, the combustion gases will have spread over the entire roof with widespread dangerously high temperatures.

- 6 JAN 76

0 1.40	20	A
0 5.00	25	A
0 3.95	25	A
0 0.67 TAX		A
1 1.02	ST	A
1 1.02	AT	A
0 0.00 CHNG		A

6183

chapter 5

HEAT VENTS

Following a disastrous fire at an automotive parts plant in 1955 there was a great deal of interest in the development of formulae for designing heat vents to prevent the spread of destructive fires over the surface of roofs of combustible construction. It was proposed to use heat vents in monitors which would divide the roof into reasonably small areas or to obtain the subdivision by draft curtains with vents in each fire curtained area. Experimental work to determine these formulae was carried out in the laboratories of the Factory Mutual Engineering Division and by other organizations. In general, it was presumed that the occupancy fire which might act as an exposure to the roof construction would be a localized fire in an area without continuity of combustibles so that sprinkler protection would normally be omitted. At the same time it was assumed that localized accumulations of combustibles might be present to offer a rather severe fire hazard not thoroughly appreciated and not properly safeguarded.

A further objective of the heat vent studies was to determine whether or not heat vents might serve to limit fire destruction in very large areas which are quite usual in modern manufacturing plants and where for reasons of the most economical production there has been great resistance to subdivision by fire walls.

The problem is very much complicated by the fact that no one knows in advance just how much exposure there will be to the roof construction and what the corresponding air temperatures will be just under the roof. This is important in attempting to estimate the heat liberation from the construction, which will increase with the temperature. Furthermore, only approximate data is at hand for estimating heat liberation for the various types of roof constructions except for the standard exposure in the Factory Mutual construction materials calorimeter.

Heat Venting Formulae

As a part of the heat vent study attempts were made to apply the more or less standardized formula for heat venting stacks. This formula is as follows:

$$A = \frac{Q}{.24\ (t_2 - t_1)\ d_2\ K\ \sqrt{2g\left(\dfrac{d_1 - d_2}{d_2}\right)H}}$$

where A — area of vent in square feet

Q — heat to be vented in btu per second

H — stack height in feet

K — orifice coefficient of vent opening

t_1 — temperature of outside air in degrees F.

t_2 — temperature of vented gases in degrees F.

d_1 — density of outside air, pounds per cubic foot

d_2 — density of vented gases, pounds per cubic foot.

This formula can be greatly simplified by making certain assumptions which are not important in regard to some of the factors involved. If we assume that the outside air temperature will be in the neighborhood of 70°F. with an air density of 0.075 pounds per cubic foot, and that the orifice coefficient will be about 0.8, the formula can be reduced to the following:

$$A = \frac{0.375\ (t_2 + 460)\ Q}{\sqrt{H}\ (t_2 - t_1)\ \sqrt{(t_2 - t_1)}}.$$

Heat Venting Experiments

When these formulae were applied to experiments where the factors were known, at least approximately, it was found that overgenerous figures for required vent areas were obtained. It had to be assumed that in the experiments the heat developed was less than anticipated because of reduced oxygen in the atmosphere and because of heat losses by radiation and conduction to the building structure. Furthermore, it was not intended to keep the building atmosphere in the normal temperature range, and it was not possible to vent all of the heat produced even if desired. A program of small scale experiments were first conducted at the Factory Mutual laboratories on a model scale, followed later by large scale tests in a 2,300-square-foot curtained section of a noncombustible fire test building. Later even larger scale tests were carried out in a special roof deck testing structure 20 feet wide and 100 feet long.

For the tests in the fire test building an area of 2,300 square feet was curtained off by sheet metal draft curtains 5 feet deep. Venting was through two roof hatches opened to 16 and 32 square feet; they discharged to atmosphere at a level about 3½ feet above the room ceiling so that the stack height was approximately 8½ feet. Gasoline from a spray nozzle was burned near the floor of the curtained area at various rates, and temperatures were recorded under the ceiling at points nearly over the fire, at points to give average temperatures throughout the curtained area, and at points just outside the curtained area. The tests were continued for only 15 minutes in order not to cause serious damage to the building at the higher gasoline rates. All temperature data were revised to reflect a common outdoor base temperature of 70°F. Ample fresh air supply was assured by an open 64-square-foot door about 80 feet away from the fire, and no tests were run except under fairly calm wind conditions and only when the open door was not exposed to any wind pressure.

Some of the results obtained from tests in which gasoline was burned at a rate of 3.5 gallons per minute are summarized in Table 3. Thermocouples outside of the draft curtain were located 2 feet away from the curtain and 1 foot below the ceiling. All other thermocouples were located 8 inches below the ceiling.

A single test was made with a 16-square-foot opening but with an extended stack of 10 feet, making a total stack height of 18½ feet. In this test the temperature outside of

Table 3: Summary of Venting Test Results

Temperatures	No Vent	16-sq.-ft. Vent	32-sq.-ft. Vent
	Temperature — °F.		
Over fire	1,430°F.	1,190°F.	1,030°F.
Average for curtained area	890	760	630
Just outside curtained area	620	315	190

the curtained area was reduced to 260°F. from the 315°F. obtained without the additional stack effect.

If we attempt to apply our simplified formula for heat vent area to the single test with the 16-square-foot vent and the gasoline rate of 3.5 gallons per minute, we first must decide what was the temperature of the gases leaving the vent. Since the vent was located a few feet laterally away from the fire, the chances are that the vent temperature was somewhat less than the temperature over the fire which was 1,190°F. It appears reasonable to assume that the vent gas temperature was about 1,080°F. The square root of the stack height, 8½ feet, is 2.91. Applying the formula:

$$A = \frac{0.375 \ (1,080 + 460) \ 3.5 \ (120,000)}{2.91 \ (1,080 - 70) \ \sqrt{1,080 - 70} \ (60)} = 36.3 \text{ square feet.}$$

The fact that this theoretical figure is much greater than the 16 square feet actually used is not surprising, because only a part of the heat produced was exhausted through the vent; otherwise the temperature outside of the fire curtain would not have risen to 315°F. Furthermore, even though the test was continued for 15 minutes and temperatures had become somewhat stabilized, there was still a significant loss of heat to the building structure.

It should be noted that in these tests, in which gasoline was burned in the form of a fine spray just above floor level, the combustion of the gasoline was practically completed inside of the building. This would not be the case when the principal source of fuel is a combustible ceiling. In a wide-spread ceiling fire there is a zone several feet deep under the ceiling where the oxygen content of the atmosphere is invariably reduced, even with a generous air supply to the building as a whole.

Vents in Combustible Roofs

For the heat vent tests involving combustible roofs, a structure was used which had been employed previously for determining flame spread characteristics of various types of roof construction. This test structure was 20 feet wide by 100 feet long with a headroom of 10 feet. The combustible roof to be tested was supported on the side walls and on a centrally located longitudinal steel beam supported in turn on steel purlins running latitudinally and spaced 6 feet 8 inches apart so that there were three purlins for every 20 feet of length. At the closed (east) end of the structure a means was provided for an exposure fire which would produce temperatures under the first 20 feet of roof length (about 400 square feet) that duplicated the standard exposure temperatures for testing the fire resistance of building construction elements. The actual temperatures attained under the directly exposed roof section as well as under the rest of the roof would, of course, be modified by heat from burning of the roof construction.

In order to test the action of heat vents, a monitor was built the full width of the test structure above the purlins with the east and west faces of the monitor 73 feet and 80 feet away respectively from the closed firing end. The monitor was roughly 7 feet high equipped with venting windows on both the east and west faces so as to permit variable venting areas up to a total of 64 square feet. The center points of the windows were 5 feet 8 inches above the underside of the roof. The west end of the test structure was left open except for a shallow metal curtain about 2 feet deep just under the roof.

Air for combustion of the exposure fire fuel (gasoline) was furnished by a blower and included additional air for

Factory Mutual Engineering Division

Figure 11. Test structure ready for monitor vent tests; vents closed.

Factory Mutual Engineering Division

Figure 12. Monitor vent test No. 4; vents open.

combustion of fuel vapors from the roof. The rate of gasoline combustion was varied in order to produce the standard exposure but was held at 2.5 gallons per minute during the period from 7 to 17 minutes, in which the maximum temperature conditions in and around the vent were obtained. Gasoline at a rate of 2.5 gallons per minute would liberate about 300,000 btu per minute. The total forced air supply of 5,600 cubic feet per minute would permit the development of only 590,000 btu per minute. Consequently, provision was made for additional air supply by natural draft by making an opening 18 inches high in one of the side walls (north) 50 feet long, extending from 30 feet to 80 feet from the firing end.

Except for one wood plank roof, all of the constructions tested in the heat vent series were on 18 gauge steel deck. These roofs had 1-inch-thick wood fiber insulation with a weatherproof outer covering of two-ply felt topped with tar and gravel. Some reinforcement was added over 30 feet of roof near the firing end to prevent loss of combustible vapors by rupture. The individual test constructions were as follows:

Test No. 1. The insulation was strip-mopped to the steel deck with asphalt applied on the average at 15 pounds per 100 square feet.

Test No. 2. This was also a strip-mopped application but with 17.1 pounds of asphalt per 100 square feet.

Test No. 3. In this test the insulation was fastened to the steel deck by a complete asphalt coverage of 24 pounds per 100 square feet.

Test No. 4. This roof had a 2-ply vapor seal of 15-pound asphalt saturated rag felt with complete mopping of asphalt above, between, and below the the felts, amounting to 22.2 pounds per 100 square feet in each one of the three coats, making a total of 84.8 pounds of asphalt between the insulation and the steel deck, including the asphalt saturant in the felts.

Test No. 5. In this test there was no steel deck but instead the roof consisted of 2-inch by 8-inch

western hemlock matched planking installed in 20
foot lengths across the structure and nailed to 2- by
6-inch wood strips fastened to the longitudinal roof
frame members. The moisture content of the wood
averaged 8.7 per cent and ranged from 6.9 per cent
to 9.9 per cent. An asphalt impregnated felt covering was fastened to the top surface for weather
protection.

Test No. 6. This test roof was a duplicate of that
in Test No. 3 but in this test the gasoline fire exposure was increased by 50 per cent so that a rate
of 3.75 gallons per minute was obtained during the
period from 7 to 17 minutes.

By the use of thermocouples and automatic temperature recorders, temperatures were taken of the atmosphere
at various points throughout the structure at distances 6
inches below the roof and in the monitor, and also at various
levels below the roof. In addition, temperatures were
recorded in the exposed steel work throughout the structure.

The amount of vent opening for each test was selected
primarily as a matter of judgement which did not always
turn out to be of the best. The actual vent opening occurred
immediately following the fusing of a 165°F. link up in the
monitor. In all of the tests, ignition of the roof occurred at
about 6 minutes after the exposure burners were turned on.
While there was some difference in the results between
the various roof types, the maximum heat noted just ahead
of the monitor usually occurred at between 12 and 15 minutes from the start of the test. The principal exception was
the wood roof test in which the maximum air temperature
occurred at 28 minutes and the maximum for the supporting steel beams at 45 minutes. This test was run for 60
minutes while the metal deck tests were run only 30 minutes, because prior to this time the metal deck insulation
over the exposure fire was so burned out that temperatures
within the structure had fallen well below their maximums.

In all of the tests with steel decks, flame and some
unburned gases came out of the vents, but the long flames
from the vents were most noticeable in the test on the roof
with the two-ply vapor seal. In this test the issuance of

flame from vents persisted for a much longer period. Because of the flames and smoke issuing from the vents, it was obvious that only a portion of the combustible gases developed were completely burned inside of the test structure.

In the case of the wood plank roof, however, flames spread under the roof to the monitor at between 7 and 8 minutes and then died back to the directly exposed section of the roof about 1 minute later. This flame spread to the monitor was repeated again at about 12 minutes and at about 21 minutes but the flaming did not persist. After about 23 or 24 minutes, temperatures in the structure did not increase substantially, but because they were still maintained at a high level, it was obvious that gases evolved from the wood were still being burned or oxidized in spite of the absence of visible flaming.

The test structure with the monitor heat vent is roughly equivalent to a 20-foot-wide strip in a flat roof building with venting monitors 150 feet apart and with the exposure fire centered between two monitors. At the fire intensity during the period from 7 to 17 minutes the heat from the exposure is less than would be obtained from two 8-foot-high stacks of slatted hardwood pallets in contact with each other. In the tests there was some heat loss to the test structure sidewalls, whereas in a large building area this side loss might not occur because the space adjacent to the sample strip might have the same exposure and the same temperatures.

For the various types of roof construction tested it was hoped to use enough vent area to prevent temperatures on the far side of the monitor (80 feet from the firing end) from exceeding about 600°F. The results of the tests are shown briefly in Table 4. The vent areas listed are those actually used but corrected for the effect of the wind, because vents subject to pressure on the windward side of the monitor could not function properly. Air temperatures shown are the 5-minute maximum averages at 20, 40, 60, 73, and 80 feet from the firing end. The difference between the temperatures at 73 feet and 80 feet show the effect of the monitor vents in cutting down the heat spread to the protected side of the monitor. For the sake of comparative

Table 4: Results of Tests With Varying Constructions and Vent Ratios

Test	Vent Area — Sq. Ft.		Maximum Average Air Temperatures Under Roof — °F.				
No.	Provided	Amount Effective	Distance From Firing End				
			20 ft.	40 ft.	60 ft.	73 ft.	80 ft.
1.	16	12.5	1,250	1,300	1,300	1,350	950
2.	32	28	1,400	1,400	1,350	1,350	610
3.	48	24	1,500	1,500	1,500	1,475	800
4.	64	63	1,650	1,500	1,500	1,460	700
5.	30	27	1,300	1,250	1,200	1,250	625
6.	61	32	1,750	1,600	1,530	1,530	650
Noncombustible roof, same firing rate, same insulating value but no monitor, at 15 minutes.			1,125	615	460	430	380

interest, roof temperatures are also shown for an earlier test on a noncombustible roof subject to the same exposure but with no monitor.

The first column in Table 5 gives an estimate based primarily on calorimeter tests of the total heat which might be developed from the various constructions when exposed at the temperature range from 20 feet to 73 feet from the firing end. These figures assume an adequate air supply to the construction, which would not be obtained in the average spreading ceiling fire. The figure for Test No. 4 (the roof with the two-ply vapor seal) is in some degree a matter of guesswork because of limited calorimeter data.

Vent Test Results

The results of these monitor heat vent tests are shown graphically in Figure 13. The total potential heat development in the test structure is plotted against the effective vent area required to maintain the protected side of the

Table 5: Estimated and Calculated Vent Areas

(Estimated areas based on results shown in Table 4 — calculated areas determined by using vent stack formula.)

Test No.	Estimated 5-min. max. Potential Heat from Roof Construction	Total Potential Heat (includes exposure fuel)	Vent area	
			Estimated	Calculated
	btu per sq. ft. per min. per sec.	btu per sec.	sq. ft.	sq. ft.
1.	450[1] 7.50[1]	15,500[2]	28[3]	80[4]
2.	550 9.16	17,800	29	92
3.	650 10.83	20,200	30	97
4.	1,800 30.00	47,600	74	233
5.	350 5.83	13,200	28	74
6.	800 13.34	26,400	34	122

Notes. [1]These figures are estimated from calorimeter tests based upon exposures from 20 feet to 73 feet from the firing end as shown in Table 4.

[2]These figures are the products of multiplying those in the preceding column by the area in square feet (1,420), plus the heat from the gasoline exposure fire (5,000 btu per second in Tests 1 to 5; 7,500 btu per second in Test No. 6).

[3]These are estimates of the amount of effective vent needed to keep the protected side of the monitor (temperatures at 80 feet from the firing end) at 600°F. or below.

[4]Based on total potential heat available, an orifice coefficient of 0.8, and a stack height of 8 feet which includes the stack effect of the fire curtain at the exit end of the structure. The vent temperature is taken as the temperature under the roof at 73 feet from the firing end. This stack formula is based on the assumption that all of the heat in the gases above ambient temperature is expelled from the vent. Area of vent calculated in this manner is obviously far too high: first, because all of the potential heat is not developed in the structure because of insufficient oxygen and, second, because the objective was to expel only enough gases to limit the temperatures on the protected side of the monitor to not over 600°F.

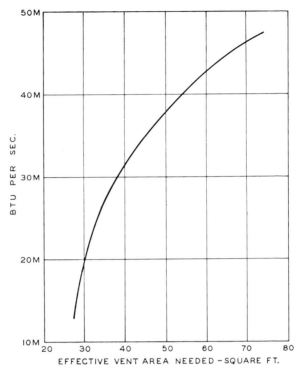

Figure 13. Effective vent areas required to maintain a temperature not over 600°F. on the protected side of the monitor (for stack height of 8 feet).

monitor at not over 600°F. The ratio of required effective vent in terms of square feet of vent per 100 square feet of roof area is 1.97, 2.04, 2.11, 5.21, and 2.39 for the insulated metal deck roofs (Test Nos. 1, 2, 3, 4, and 6). For the wood plank roof (Test No. 5) the ratio is 1.97.

It is interesting to note that the vent area required in Test No. 6 is greater than in Test No. 3. The roof constructions were the same — a complete asphalt mop at 24 pounds per 100 square feet — but the exposure fire was increased by 50 per cent in Test No. 6 with correspondingly higher temperatures under the roof. Consequently, the amount of vent area needed is closely related to the probable degree of exposure. This in turn is governed to some extent by the available air supply to an exposing occupancy fire and to the fuel gases evolved from the heated roof construction. While in an ordinary manufacturing building with a headroom from 20 feet upwards there would be a better internal air supply than in the 10-foot-high test structure, it is quite probable that in the tests, with the forced air to the gasoline burners plus some air from natural draft through the 18-inch-high opening in the north side of the test structure, there was as much available air supply as could be expected in a building twice the height of the test structure.

Assuming that the exposure used in these tests was the maximum which might ordinarily be expected in practice, it is indicated that the vent ratios which should be provided in terms of area of vent to area of roof are : 1 to 50 for metal deck with strip mop adhesive, 1 to 47 or possibly 1 to 45 for a complete mopping, 1 to 20 for two-ply complete mopped vapor seal, and 1 to 50 for a wood plank roof. These figures presume that all of the vent area would be effective, i.e., not nullified by wind pressure.

Unless means are provided to prevent adverse wind pressure on the vents, the area of the vents should be increased with half of the vents facing in one direction and half in the other direction. In one of the tests (No. 3), for example, the wind pressure made one half of the vents totally ineffective. So to compensate for a similar maximum adverse condition that may be experienced in actual practice, the vent areas should be doubled. These vent ratios from tests with monitor vents should be equally effective with subdivision of areas by draft curtains which should be installed with tight connections to the roof.

To provide effective automatic heat vents in the ratios indicated would be an expensive procedure, particularly in an existing building where draft curtains of the proper depth might be impractical. If lesser ratios are provided, it would mean that considerable chance would be taken that the exposure would be relatively mild, that there would be only a small probability of the simultaneous occurrence of fire with adverse wind conditions, and that prompt alarm and response by a well trained fire department could be expected. Certainly, for metal deck roofs with asphalt coated vapor seals, the only sensible protection remedy is the installation of automatic sprinklers.

Heat vents with draft curtains would be advisable to separate extra hazard processes from other areas, even with sprinklers installed, where effective cut-offs by fire walls are impractical. Heat vents, especially with cross monitors, might also be of considerable benefit in large high value areas to reduce the chance of very large fire losses — with or without sprinklers.

Noncombustible Fire Breaks

In order to prevent fire spread over the inside of a large roof area, noncombustible fire breaks have been suggested as a simple solution. This dubious remedy can be analyzed by the following example: Suppose we have an insulated metal deck roof with the insulation fastened to the deck by a complete asphalt mopping weighing 24 pounds per 100 square feet. Let us assume that the metal deck roof area is divided into 150-foot-long sections by 20-foot-wide, 4-inch-thick reinforced concrete sections or strips. We may also assume that the metal deck roof becomes ignited at the center of one of the roof sections and that the fire spreads the distance of 75 feet to the concrete strip. To determine the value of the concrete break we need only to consider a strip of roof 1 foot wide, that is 75 square feet of metal deck and 20 square feet of concrete.

The heat developed by the complete combustion of the asphalt mopping would be roughly 650 btu per square foot per minute at an exposure of 1,500°F. Let us assume further that because of insufficient oxygen a fire in the roof can develop only 450 btu per square foot per minute. Then for 75 square feet the heat production would be 33,750 btu per minute. In order to prevent ignition on the far side of the concrete let it be assumed that the temperature of the air at the concrete surface would have to drop to 700°F. So to be successful the temperature of the concrete strip surface must decrease gradually over the 20-foot width from 1,500° to 700°F.

Hot combustion products travelling along under a roof or ceiling can lose heat by radiation to the building and to the building's contents and by conduction to the roof and its supporting structural elements. The heat loss by radiation, while appreciable, is still small and can be ignored because the heat output values as determined in the Factory Mutual construction materials calorimeter are net output values after radiation losses. Heat losses by conduction may be divided into two parts, conduction from layer to layer in the hot gas volume and from an extremely thin layer in actual contact with the underside of the roof surface. Since the total volume of combustion gases in our example produces a layer which may be several feet thick, the efficiency of heat transfer by conduction to the concrete surface is quite low.

Even if we assumed that heat transfer conditions were ideal, the concrete construction cannot absorb heat at a rate higher than can be dissipated through the material by conduction. The thermal conductivity of a 1 to 4 concrete mixture is about 0.44 btu per square foot per degree F. per 1-inch thickness per hour. With a 4-inch-thick section of 20 square feet and with an under surface temperature of 1,500°F. at one end and 700°F. at the other, and with a top surface (exterior) temperature of 70°F., the heat loss through the concrete could not exceed about 380 btu per minute.

The concrete strip could lose a substantial amount of heat by radiation with the under surface varying from 1,500°F. to 700°F. The concrete radiation emissivity coefficient would be about 0.65 so that we find by calculation the maximum radiation loss to the building floor and contents would be 2,340 btu per minute for 20 square feet. The actual radiation loss would be somewhat less than this because of the low-order radiation opacity of the combustion gases.

A large amount of heat would be required to bring the temperature of the 4-inch-thick concrete to the temperature which we have assumed, since the 20 square feet of concrete would weigh about 960 pounds. With a specific heat of 0.20 the total heat energy required would be approximately 197,-000 btu. Regardless of the specific heat, the flow of heat into and through the concrete cannot be any greater than the conductivity will allow. Even if the concrete were only $\frac{1}{8}$-inch thick, the rate of conducted heat would be only about 12,000 btu per minute.

The total of these theoretical losses is still far below the heat production rate of 33,700 btu per minute. Consequently, we must conclude that noncombustible fire breaks are not of much value by themselves except possibly in marginal cases where conditions are not very favorable for fire spread.

chapter 6

AUTOMATIC SPRINKLER PROTECTION

The annual waste from fire damage has been substantially reduced by the development and improvement in sprinkler systems. This has been brought out very clearly by Factory Mutual Engineering Division fire records for industrial properties. The first decided reduction was in mid-nineteenth century and was due to the use of perforated pipe systems in rooms with recognized fire hazards, and then again from about 1875 to 1910 due to the gradual installation of automatic sprinkler systems. The overall reduction in industrial fire losses was from about one-half dollar down to only two or three cents per hundred dollars of insured property in recent years. During this period of about one hundred years other very important factors in loss reduction were better recognition of hazards, strengthened water supplies, organization and training of public and private fire departments, and availability of improved extinguishers for manual use.

This chapter deals with the history of sprinkler protection, covering only the highlights from the earliest systems to the modern standard automatic sprinkler. Information is presented to show the difference in distribution between the present standard sprinkler and the previous (old-style) sprinkler. Shown also are some comparative fire test results and the Factory Mutual approval standards developed for the new sprinkler.

Early History

A system of sprinklers using pipes fed from an elevated gravity tank was patented in London in 1806 by John Carey.* The "sprinklers" were somewhat similar to the per-

---

The Factory Mutuals, 1835-1935 (Providence, R. I.: Manufacturers Mutual Fire Insurance Company, 1935).

forated sprinkler which is used today on the ordinary garden watering can. Flow of water from the tank to the sprinklers was controlled by means of a weight-operated valve, the weight normally held up by a system of cords and pulleys, the cords passing through the area to be protected. When a cord burned, the weight dropped and opened the valve.

A somewhat refined sprinkler system was patented by William Congreve in 1809 (British Patent No. 3201). In addition to strings or cords, the system utilized wires and pulleys, the wires containing fusible links consisting of two thin pieces of metal "about the size of a half-crown" held together by a fusible metal made up of eight parts bismuth, five parts lead, and three parts tin with a melting point of 190°F. Congreve also described a means of releasing weights by the expansion of mercury. He also showed sprinkler devices, including perforated false ceilings, perforated piping at high levels around the room, and devices with flattened and spread apertures to spray out into the room from near the ceiling in a manner similar to our present day sidewall sprinklers. In addition, he used a wide coverage sprinkler device in the center of the room very similar in design to a rotating lawn sprinkler. For large and spacious rooms, he suggested division into compartments, each with its own fuse link, valves, and "showers" so that "the extent of the remedy shall be limited to the extent of the evil."

Whether any of these systems attained widespread successful use is questionable. Stretching cords or wires caused the valves to leak, and the valves frequently stuck in the shut position.

The first sprinkler systems to be used in this country were of the perforated pipe type and were installed at the plant of the Proprietors of the Locks and Canals at Lowell, Massachusetts, in about 1852. These systems were extended and improved through the efforts of James B. Francis who developed a system using pipe with perforations 1/10 inch in diameter and spaced 9 inches apart alternately on different sides and so placed as to deliver a jet of water at an angle slightly above the horizontal. Sometime later, before

1880, the Factory Mutual Companies developed a system using wrought iron pipes with holes 1/12th inch in diameter and spaced 3 inches apart alternately on top of the pipe, with the holes set at 30 degrees from the vertical.

From 1874, beginning with development work and patents by Henry S. Parmelee of New Haven, Connecticut, to about 1900, there were many attempts to perfect a reliable individually automatic sprinkler. The first sprinkler to be used successfully over a long period, however, was the Grinnell "glass button" type appearing in 1890. Following 1900 most of the changes in sprinklers were in the line of improvements and refinements rather than drastic design changes. From 1920 to 1950 the principal innovations in sprinkler design were the Grinnell "quartz bulb" type, which appeared in 1924; the Globe "Saveall," actuated by the melting of an organic compound instead of fusible metal, first produced in 1931, and finally the Grinnell "Duraspeed," much faster than other sprinklers of the same temperature rating due to a larger ratio of surface area to mass in the actuating linkage.

The latest really drastic change in sprinkler design was the result of development and experimental work at the Factory Mutual laboratories during the years 1947 to 1950.* This change had to do with water distribution only and involved only the sprinkler deflector. The new development, together with information on the advantages in fire control, was passed on to all manufacturers of approved sprinklers in November 1950. Manufacturers then worked on deflector designs to adapt the new type of distribution to their individual requirements. The new sprinklers were designated spray sprinklers, now the industry standard.

The Automatic Sprinkler

The automatic sprinkler in general use is essentially an automatic water flow control valve with an orifice and deflector to discharge water at a prescribed rate and in a def-

---

*Norman J. Thompson, "New Developments in Upright Sprinklers," NFPA *Quarterly,* July 1952, pp 5-18.

inite distribution pattern. The standard valve size is designated as nominal "½ inch" and discharges approximately 57 gallons per minute at a water pressure of 100 pounds per square inch. A smaller size with half of this discharge rate is manufactured for installation in low hazard occupancies. More recently, a somewhat larger size has been made available for high hazard occupancies so that heavier discharge rates can be obtained without requiring excessively high water pressures.

Mode of Operation

The valve of a typical automatic sprinkler is controlled usually by a combination of struts, links, and fusible metal so as to operate when the fusible metal is heated to approximately 165°F. The reason for selecting a 165°F. operating temperature is to prevent premature operation of the sprinkler because of weakening of the fusible metal under load at temperatures within 30°F. below its melting point. Other types of sprinklers not subject to such failure are available with temperature ratings as low as 135°F. These sprinklers operate because of the pressure in a quartz bulb due to expansion of a liquid or because of the melting of a chemical compound. Sprinklers are also manufactured with temperature ratings up to 500°F. for locations normally at temperatures above the ordinary atmospheric range.

The actuating mechanism of a sprinkler is usually under a compressive force resulting from tension in the frame, although in the case of sprinklers using fusible metals the fusible element is usually under tension. The purpose of this frame tension is to throw parts of the actuating mechanism clear when the sprinkler operates; otherwise, parts may lodge on the deflector, thus distorting the distribution pattern.

The operating time of any sprinkler is governed principally by the operating temperature and thermal lag of the heat sensitive element. Regardless of the actual operating temperature of the element or "link," it requires a definite amount of heat input to bring it up to the operating temperature. The required amount of heat is proportional to the weight or mass of the link, and the time is also governed by the initial temperature of the link, the relation between the rated operating temperature and the temperature of hot gases to which it is exposed, and by the velocity of these gases as they move around the link. The greater the ratio of surface area to mass of the link, the faster it will operate under any given set of conditions.

Distribution Patterns

Old-style Sprinklers: The distribution pattern of the older type sprinkler (up to 1953) was such as to throw about 60 per cent of the discharge upward and outward to the ceiling within a radius of from 2 to 3 feet when the sprinkler was located 8 inches below the ceiling and was operated at a water pressure of 15 pounds per square inch. Most of this water ran along the ceiling for a few inches and then fell to the floor in large drops or even in small streams to give generous wetting to the floor or objects on the floor up to a radius of 3 to 4 feet. Because of the downward discharge of the remaining 40 per cent, there was a fair amount of wetting up to radii of 5 to 6 feet, and some wetting up to about an 8-foot radius. Since the portion of the water falling from the ceiling was in the form of large drops, it was relatively inefficient in cooling the hot gases from a fire at high levels. As the flowing pressure on any sprinkler is increased, the discharge has a greater range or "reach" and the water is more finely broken up.

Standard Sprinklers: The present standard sprinkler, first known as the "spray sprinkler," has an entirely different discharge pattern. The water leaves the deflector in a solid spray pattern with an included angle of about 180 degrees. Little or no water is discharged against the ceiling. Consequently, practically all of the discharge can be distributed to the best effectiveness. The result is more uniformity in distribution over the area covered and a somewhat greater range than the older type deflector. Because no water is directed against the ceiling, the distribution pattern is only slightly altered by placing the sprinkler at different distances below the ceiling. Since all the water is discharged in a solid hemispherical pattern below the deflector and because the water is all in relatively small droplets, the upper level cooling is quite superior to the old type. Like the old type, the range and water breakup of the standard sprinkler is increased with increasing pressure.

Since all the water from the standard sprinkler is discharged in one direction only (below the deflector level), the sprinklers for installation in an upright position cannot be inverted for use in the pendent position. Consequently, standard sprinklers are made in two types, one for upright and one for pendent installation. They are equal in distribution characteristics and fire control effectiveness.

Because of the proven superior effectiveness of the standard sprinkler, the area coverage per sprinkler has been extended as compared to the old type, and from 1955 on almost all new sprinkler installations in this country were made with the new standard sprinkler.

The Standard Sprinkler

Since hundreds of fire tests under widely varying conditions had shown that the best protection occurred when the maximum amount of water was discharged onto the burning material and when the products of combustion especially at high levels were subject to maximum cooling, the standard sprinkler in the development process was designed to attain these two objectives — at least in a satisfactory degree. At the same time, it was desired to reach a high degree of uniformity with multiple sprinkler operation.

Distribution Tests

To determine if these objectives were met, the minimum average distribution at various distances away from a point directly under a sprinkler was established as is shown in Figure 14. This average distribution was obtained with a sprinkler located 8 inches under a smooth ceiling and sup-

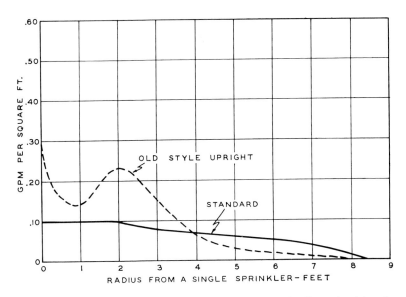

Figure 14. Distribution density of standard and old-style sprinklers with the density measured 48 inches below the deflectors and at a discharge of 15 gallons per minute.

plied with water at 15 gallons per minute, and with a rotating carriage supporting up to 12 one-foot-square collecting measuring pans 4 feet below the sprinkler deflector. The distribution of a typical old style sprinkler is also shown in Figure 14 for comparison. The decided hump in the curve for the old type sprinkler is due mostly to the water which discharges against the ceiling and falls almost vertically therefrom.

These average density measurements throughout the entire 360 degrees on circles of increasing diameter do not tell the full story in regard to uniformity within each circle. Consequently, a simplified method of checking this feature consisted of measuring the amount of water collected in a 4-foot-square aggregate of 16 one-square-foot pans located 7 feet below sprinklers spaced 10 feet apart on centers. This square pan setup was centered under four sprinklers for one series of tests and centered under two sprinklers on a branch line for the other series. Distribution tests with this setup were run at three different rates of water flow, namely 12.8, 16.6, and 24 gallons per minute. In order to pass these tests, a candidate sprinkler for approval should not produce less than one per cent of the total sprinkler discharge per single pan on the average for the 16-pan setup.

Considering the distribution tests as a whole, deviations in density above the average are not important unless they are so great as to result in water deficiencies at other points. Since the distribution curve in Figure 14 accounts for only 12 gallons per minute out of a total flow of 15 gallons per minute, it is practicable to meet the requirements. Between 0 and 2 feet radius there is considerable leeway allowed because the area involved is so small. The relative unimportance of this small area has been confirmed in fire tests with sprinklers which showed a very scant distribution density within 2 feet.

The Factory Mutual approval standards further require that little or no water should be thrown into any pan beyond a diameter of 16 feet at a discharge rate of 15 gallons per minute when the pans are located 4 feet below the sprinkler; and no water should be thrown in such a manner as to wet an adjacent sprinkler 7 feet away at the same elevation at a flow of either 15 or 30 gallons per minute.

Fire Tests

In order to confirm the performance of a sprinkler based on distribution tests, fire tests were called for. Except for a single test over a fire involving only a gasoline spray burning at a rate of 1.75 gallons per minute, each of the other tests was made with a Douglas fir crib, elevated over a gasoline spray fire, which could be burned at three degrees of intensity. The crib was placed 7½ feet below the sprinkler deflectors and was centered under four sprinklers or between two sprinklers on a branch line depending on the test. The crib was constructed mostly of nominal 2- by 4-inch wood and was 4 feet square by about 2 feet high, and weighed about 300 pounds not including a pair of 4- by 6-inch wood

Factory Mutual Engineering Division

Figure 15. Typical test fire to prove value of the standard sprinkler.

supports. The gasoline flow rates were 0.73, 0.90, and 1.31 gallons per minute for tests at 12.8, 16.6, and 24 gallons per minute sprinkler flow respectively. For each condition limiting standards were developed for the maximum number of sprinklers opened, the maximum crib weight loss, and the maximum sustained 5-minute temperature at the ceiling over the fire.* In addition to the function of these fire tests

---

*For further information on the development and performance of the standard sprinkler, the reader is referred to the article, "New Developments in Upright Sprinklers," by Norman J. Thompson in the NFPA *Quarterly*, July 1952, pp. 5-18.

Table 6: Fire Test Results — Standard vs. Old-Style Sprinklers

(Comparison of fire test results with old-style sprinklers (OS) and new standard sprinklers (SS) under a noncombustible ceiling 15½ feet high. All sprinklers on 10- by 10-foot spacing. All tests with 300-pound, 4- by 4-foot wood crib except one on gasoline only.)

Sprinkler Type	Fire Location	Gasoline Fuel Flow gpm	Wood Moisture %	Water Supply		No. of Sprinklers Opened	Total Water Flow gpm	Crib Weight Loss lbs.	Ceiling Temperature (5-min. max.) °F.
				psi	gpm per Sprinkler				
OS	Centered under 4 sprinklers	0.73	15	5	12.8	19	245	170	1,020
SS		"	14	"	"	11	141	40	530
OS	Centered under 4 sprinklers	0.90	15	15	22.1	12	265	140	1,120
SS		"	15	8.5	16.6	11	182	65	600
OS	Centered under 2 sprinklers	0.90	15	15	22.1	11	243	130	1,050
SS		"	14	8.5	16.6	9	149	40	600
OS	Centered under 4 sprinklers	1.31	14	31.5	32.0	11	352	175	1,350
SS		"	14	17.75	24.0	11	264	70	850
OS	Centered under 4 sprinklers	1.75	no crib	31.5	32.0	11	352	—	1,200
SS*		"	"	17.75	24.0	15	360	—	1,400

*This was one of the earlier experimental spray sprinklers with a relatively coarse discharge, and thus did not give the best upper level cooling. In one rare isolated incident an approved production spray sprinkler actually extinguished this gasoline fire.

in checking the distribution of the sprinklers, they also gave valuable information on the water breakup of the sprinkler discharge. If the breakup is too fine, the water will not penetrate down through the fire draft, and the crib weight losses will be too high. On the other hand, if the water drops are too coarse, the upper level cooling will suffer, and ceiling temperatures will be excessive. This latter condition prevailed in the results of the last test shown in Table 6.

chapter 7

SPRINKLERS — HOW THEY WORK

In order to understand the role of automatic sprinklers in the control and extinguishment of fires, it is advisable to review briefly some of the objectives of sprinkler protection. The first, naturally, is to extinguish the fire as quickly as possible, and, if that cannot be done, then to control and confine it so as to prevent its lateral spread. We are also interested in protecting all elements of building construction and occupancy against damage from exposure to the fire, and, furthermore, to accomplish these objectives with the minimum of sprinklers in operation, thus conserving the water supply pressure and keeping possible water damage to a minimum. Some fires, such as those in volatile flammable liquids or in some other hazardous materials, cannot be extinguished by sprinklers, so that effective action would be limited to protecting materials and building elements exposed to the fire.

The beneficial action of the water spray from a standard sprinkler may be divided into four principal effects: direct wetting and cooling of combustibles, cooling of the atmosphere, cooling of exposed building elements and contents, and reducing oxygen content in the air. Certain of these effects can only be obtained at the expense of others.

Direct Wetting and Cooling

The most important effect on a fire in ordinary combustibles is that of direct wetting and cooling of the burning combustibles themselves so as to extinguish the fire. In addition, the water spray can also wet the surfaces of unburned material just outside of the fire zone preventing or at least delaying ignition of the exposed material. Even if the combustibles originally burning are not sufficiently wetted to produce immediate extinguishment, the spread of fire is prevented and the exposure from the fire is reduced. Closely related is the action of water spray in preventing fire spread by soaking into uninvolved absorbent materials in the vicinity of active combustion, especially paper and other fibrous products. To a somewhat lesser extent the same holds true for unfinished wood surfaces, but with no such advantage in cases where the wood is painted or otherwise waterproofed.

Since the exact location of any possible fire is never known in advance, it is obvious that the distribution of the water spray over any part of the area in which a fire might occur must be uniform, and that the water spray drops must be large enough to travel down to the combustible surfaces against the rising currents of hot products of combustion.

Cooling the Atmosphere

Automatic sprinklers also are effective in cooling the ambient atmosphere, particularly the upper levels under the ceiling or roof. The cooler this upper level atmosphere, the less chance there is of initiating or sustaining fire in combustible construction or of badly distorting supporting steel work. Furthermore, there is less chance of operating sprinklers unnecessarily outside of the immediate fire zone. Cooling of the atmosphere is due principally to absorption of heat by the evaporation of water from the spray drops. This evaporation and cooling is improved not only by good distribution of the water spray but also by increasing the total surface area of the drops. However, for any given rate of water discharge from a sprinkler the only way to increase surface area is to decrease the drop size. While decreased drop size, or increased atomization, has advantages in cooling the atmosphere, smaller drops have less ability to maintain their initial velocities, and their terminal velocities as free falling bodies are also reduced. Thus, if drop size is reduced too much, the proportionate number of drops able to penetrate to the burning material down through the fire updraft is correspondingly reduced to the point where effective wetting action on burning combustibles is made impossible; there must be some compromise in sprinkler protection between cooling by increased atomization and effective range of the water drops.

Cooling Exposed Elements

Water spray from sprinklers is beneficial in cooling elements of building structure or equipment to prevent damage from fire exposure. In order for this cooling to be effective the surfaces to be protected must be subject to direct impingement of water in most cases. For maximum effectiveness the water spray must be reasonably well distributed at a substantial density over the surfaces. Since the upward velocity of the products of combustion increases with overall fire intensity, it is sometimes necessary to place the sprinklers relatively close to the surfaces to be protected when the exposure is severe.

Where very severe fires might occur, especially in buildings with high ceilings, the only practical solution is the use of sprinklers not only at the ceiling but at intermediate levels so that the water drops will have only a short distance to travel. For these very severe exposure fires increasing the water density at the ceiling alone by the use of much higher than normal pressures is of dubious advantage, because the higher the pressure on the sprinkler the greater the atomization and the less the proportion of the discharge which will penetrate down through the fire draft. As a general rule pressures on sprinkler heads over 30 pounds per square inch produce little gain unless the distances between the sprinklers and the surfaces to be protected are limited to about 10 feet and preferably less. (This does not apply to narrow angle spray nozzles which have a much greater "reach" than standard sprinklers with an included angle of about 180 degrees). The principal advantage in high sprinkler pressures is reducing the number of sprinklers which may open on account of superior cooling of the atmosphere, but the effect on the fire may not be increased substantially unless the fire is of small to moderate size (less than 300,000 btu per minute, roughly) or the clearance between the sprinklers and the fire is limited to 10 feet or possibly 12 feet.

Reduction of Oxygen Content

An important action in fire control by automatic sprinklers is the return of oxygen deficient atmosphere from upper levels to the fire itself — particularly in areas of low headroom. Fire intensity is reduced as the oxygen content of the air supply is decreased, and flaming combustion may cease altogether when the percentage of oxygen is lowered to about two thirds of normal. In a fire the hot products of combustion (high in carbon dioxide and water vapor and low in oxygen) rise to levels close to the ceiling and then spread out. While the discharge from a standard sprinkler is not very efficient as an air mover, the falling drops do function to bring part of the upper atmosphere downward mixing with the lower level atmosphere on the way down. The greater the distance below the ceiling, the less the oxygen reduction at low levels. With identical occupancy fires, sprinkler protection has been proved to be more effective in areas of low instead of high headroom. One of the principal reasons for this greater effectiveness is the return of oxygen deficient atmosphere to the fire, although some credit is due to the faster operation of sprinklers and the shorter travel of water drops from the sprinkler to the fire.

A somewhat lesser factor in oxygen reduction is the evaporation from the drops in the sprinkler discharge which passes through the hot combustion gases. This water vapor is added to that occurring in the combustion products. In general, oxygen reduction due to the presence of water vapor is important only in the high temperature zones, i.e., directly over the fire and in the layer of spreading gases under the ceiling. In zones where the temperature falls to well below 180°F. the added effect from water vapor is not very important. Consequently, a deficiency in oxygen in the air supply returning to a fire at a low level is primarily due to the consumption of oxygen by the fire itself and the presence of carbon dioxide but not due to substantial dilution by water vapor.

About twenty-five years ago experiments were performed in an attempt to make use of the oxygen deficiency in combustion products by returning them to the fire with the aid of water spray nozzles.* Various arrangements of nozzles, baffles, and ducts were tried, and in some instances encouraging results were obtained with fires in pans of motor gasoline. After successful trials on a small scale, but which seemed to involve an inordinate amount of sheet metal work, it was concluded that the best commercial application of the principle would be in controlling or extinguishing fires in extra-hazardous processes where dangerous flow rates of volatile flammable liquids might be expected. Such processes would include oil extraction equipment, especially in the distillation and recovery stages Consequently, a test setup was made in which gasoline could be flowed at high rates from an elevated point down over simulated process equipment.

Gasoline was discharged by direct pumping through an open tee fitting so as to fall over a vertical single row of empty 50-gallon drums about 20 feet high. This vertical row of drums was surrounded by a rectangular sheet metal enclosure 17 feet square and extending from 10 feet to about 30 feet above the floor level. Four narrow angle spray nozzles having a "solid" conical discharge pattern with an included angle of about 60 degrees were placed inside the enclosure. Each nozzle was placed so as to cover effectively one quarter of the 17-foot-square enclosure and was located at the 30-foot elevation. The water discharge rate for each nozzle was about 106 gallons per minute at 50 pounds per square inch and 75 gallons per minute at 25 pounds per square inch. Each one of these nozzles, centered in an 8-foot-square tunnel, was capable of moving about 20,000 cubic feet of air per

---

*Reference: U. S. Patents 2,259,500, October 21, 1941 and 2,283,775, May 19, 1942.

minute with a free entrance and discharge at 50 pounds per square inch nozzle pressure.

The procedure in running the tests was to pump gasoline at varying rates from the open tee over the vertical row of drums. A wad of gasoline-soaked waste just below the bottom drum was the ignition source. The tests were run in a building of noncombustible construction 40 feet by 60 feet by 33 feet high with two roof hatches of 28 square feet each. In all of the tests there was an ample supply of fresh air from large, wide open doors. As soon as the gasoline flowing down over the drums was ignited the flames enveloped the entire row of drums and quickly reached a high intensity as the heat from the fire on the lower drums preheated gasoline flowing down at the higher levels. A valve controlling the water supply to the nozzles was opened at a time when a 165°F. sprinkler would have opened at the spray nozzle elevation.

Tests were run at varying gasoline flow rates up to 15 gallons per minute (about 1,750,000 btu per minute). In the first of the tests roof hatches were closed, and then later both hatches were kept open. It was found that as the fuel rate was increased, increasingly higher pressures were necessary on the spray nozzles in order to overcome and reverse the direction of the fire draft. With the 15 gallons per minute gasoline rate, a water pressure of nearly 50 pounds per square inch was needed. Prior to draft reversal there was some effect on the fire but without extinguishment. As soon as the travel of the products of combustion was reversed, the fire quickly went out but the water discharge was maintained for safety, because at first the room seemed to be well filled with gasoline fumes. As soon as room temperatures had returned to somewhere near normal the water supply was shut off.

Fire involving gasoline flow rates from 7.5 to 15 gallons per minute were quickly extinguished. Extinguishment at 5 gallons per minute or less was not successful. This is undoubtedly due to an insufficient oxygen reduction at the lower fire rates. However, in the case of the smaller fires which could not be extinguished, temperatures were reduced to low levels so that there would be no exposure damage from the remaining fire.

As far as is known there have been no industrial applications of this special method — probably due to the cost of sheet metal work, the probable interference in some cases of the sheet metal with accessibility to the process equipment, the inability of the method to extinguish small to moderate sized fires, and the potential explosion hazard which inevitably would follow immediately the extinguishment of a large fire in volatile flammable liquids. However, the tests of the method did show what an important role the combustion products from a fire could play in decreasing fire intensity, sometimes to the point of extinguishment.

chapter 8

OPERATING TIMES OF SPRINKLERS

This chapter discusses operating times of sprinklers, which are influenced by the temperature rating of the sprinklers, by their thermal lag, by the velocity of hot air movement around the sprinklers, and by the distance between the sprinklers and the burning combustibles. The last named factor is closely associated with the ceiling height of the building.

Temperature Rating and Thermal Lag

The operating times of sprinklers, even of the same temperature rating, vary considerably depending on the design of the sprinklers. This variation, even under identical fire conditions, is due to the difference in thermal lag of the temperature sensitive element. The amount of heat which must be transferred to the element depends upon its mass whereas the rate of heat transfer is governed principally by the surface area of the element, since the transfer of heat is primarily by convection and conduction with radiation a factor of minor importance, except possibly in fast fires of high intensity. Consequently, the sprinkler with the highest ratio of surface area to mass in the temperature sensitive element will operate the soonest under the same fire conditions.

Figure 16 shows the operating times plotted against temperatures of the surrounding atmosphere for a few of the approved standard sprinklers when located about 10 to 12 feet above the fire. These results were obtained in actual fire tests with sprinklers located approximately 7 feet away laterally from the fire center so that they were influenced in some degree by the lateral movement of hot gases under the ceiling as well as the temperature of the gases. The

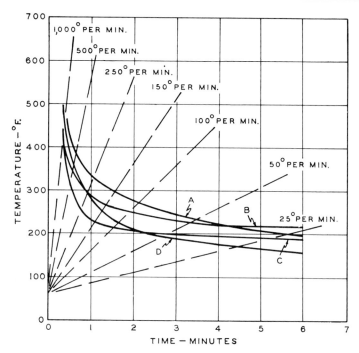

Figure 16. Operating Times of Standard Sprinklers

Curve A — Slow 165°F.   Curve B — Fast 212°F.
Curve C — Fast 165°F.   Curve D — Bulb 135°F.

dashed lines on the graph are presented as a rough guide to the average rate of temperature rise although the actual changes in temperature would be more accurately shown by curved lines. Naturally, if a fire occurs directly under a sprinkler, especially where there is a low ceiling, the sprinkler will operate faster than if the fire were centered under four sprinklers. In the latter case, the sprinklers would be 7 feet or more away horizontally from the center of the fire, where both temperatures and velocity of warm air movement are reduced.

It will be noted from Figure 16 that there is a large difference in operating time between the slowest and the fastest approved sprinklers in the 165°F. rating. The time interval is most pronounced when the rates of temperature rise are less than 150°F. per minute. In fact at the rate of temperature rise of 50°F. per minute the fast sprinkler will operate at 2.8 minutes whereas the slow sprinkler will require 3.5 minutes. It may also be noted that at rates of temperature rise in excess of 40°F. per minute the fast sprinkler in the 212°F. rating will operate sooner than the slow sprinkler in the 165°F. rating.

Since the operating times shown in Figure 16 were obtained in actual fire tests involving ordinary combustibles, the operating times are faster than would have been obtained in laboratory tests with dry air. This is because the products of combustion contain substantial percentages of water vapor. This water vapor in gases at temperatures above 212°F. will condense on the relatively cool parts of the sprinkler, and the high heat of condensation will be released causing the sprinkler to operate much sooner than in dry air.

Hot Gas Velocity

The influence of the rate of hot air movement on the operating time of sprinklers is not generally appreciated. A rapidly growing fire produces hot gases at a higher volume rate at any given time than the small fire or slowly growing fire. The effect of this can be observed by watching sparks in the products of combustion from a fire as they reach the ceiling zone and then move away laterally underneath the ceiling. For most small to moderate-sized fires in ordinary combustibles these lateral air velocities under a horizontal smooth ceiling run around the order of 1 to 10 feet per second within 5 to 7 feet away from a point over the center of the fire, and then decrease roughly according to the square of the distance at points further removed from the fire. If the ceiling is broken up by deep joists or beams, the gases will travel along the channels so that there will not be as much decrease in velocity in the channels.

To give an idea how much the rate of hot air movement past a sprinkler will affect its operating time, tests have shown that an atmosphere heated to 220°F. passing a typical approved sprinkler in the 165°F. rating at 2 feet per second will operate it in about 6 minutes, whereas with the same temperature but at three times the velocity (six feet per second) the operation time will be reduced to about 1 minute. Since both the temperature and the velocity of movement of hot gases decrease rapidly with distance away from the fire, the operating time of sprinklers is very much increased as this distance increases. Therefore, the more effective the action of sprinklers, particularly in preventing fire spread, the better the chances are the total number of sprinklers to be opened will be reduced.

Effect of Ceiling Height

Figure 17 shows the effect of ceiling height on the rate and degree of temperature buildup and the consequent effect on operating time of sprinklers. The test fires were in double 8-foot-high stacks of standard 4-foot by 4-foot slatted hardwood pallets (the same test fires reported in Figure 10). In Figure 17, however, the temperatures shown at the ceiling are about 7 feet away laterally from a point over the fire center, or about in the position of sprinklers with the fire centered under four sprinklers on a 10-foot by 10-foot spacing.

While the fires in both cases appeared to be identical in their progress there was a 1-minute difference in the time ceiling temperatures reached 140°F. and almost 1½ minutes difference at 200°F. From 200°F. onward the curve for the low ceiling fire shows an increase of about 250°F. per minute whereas the curve for the high ceiling fire shows a temperature rise rate of about 110°F. per minute. It might be assumed that the fires would open sprinklers at about 5½ minutes for the high ceiling. However, because the lateral rate of movement of hot gases under a high ceiling is substantially less than under a low ceiling, the time of sprinkler operation cannot be figured from temperature data alone. Consequently, in this example the opening time for spinklers under the high ceiling could be more than 7½ minutes.

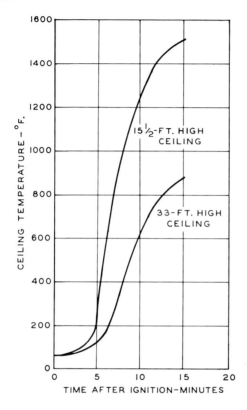

Figure 17.   Effect of Ceiling Height on Sprinkler Operating Times

Test fires identical double 8-foot stacks of wooden pallets — ceiling temperatures recorded 7 feet laterally from center of fire.

For fires less intense than in these examples the rates of temperature increase would be lessened in both cases but sprinklers over a fire under a low ceiling would still open well ahead of sprinklers under high ceiling conditions. The lesson from this, if any, is that it is better to design buildings with headroom sufficient to allow only a modest clearance (3 feet or somewhat more) above any probable occupancy. This subject of clearance between sprinklers and occupancy will be discussed again later.

chapter 9

EFFECT OF CLEARANCE BETWEEN
SPRINKLERS AND CEILING ON PROTECTION

The distance at which sprinklers are located below the ceiling is an important factor in determining the effectiveness of the protection in the event of fire. The closer sprinklers are placed to the ceiling, the faster the operating time of the first sprinklers to open. However, except for continuous smooth ceilings, location close to the ceiling is more likely to result in serious interference to lateral distribution by structural members. For the old-style sprinklers, which throw about 60 per cent of the discharge upwards, the distribution is badly affected even with smooth ceilings. For both types of sprinklers the optimum clearance under ceilings is in the general range of from 7 to 10 inches.

The conditions are changed considerably if the ceiling is broken up by beams, purlins, or joists to form narrow bays or channels, or if divided into panels or pockets by beams framed into girders. It is quite possible, in the case of a combustible ceiling on deep beams, for a fire of moderate to severe intensity to ignite the ceiling and spread a considerable distance, even from one side of the building to the other, if the location and arrangement of the sprinklers are not suited to the conditions. In any event, without proper design of the sprinkler system, hot products of combustion may build up and travel an excessive distance along the channels before the sprinklers in the immediate vicinity of the fire are affected sufficiently to operate. It is obvious that for such conditions special attention must be given to clearances between the sprinklers and the ceiling as well as to the distance between sprinklers in rows at right angles to the beams. In some extreme cases, particularly with deep beams and bays less than 7 or 8 feet wide, it may be necessary to obtain the proper clearance between the sprinklers and the ceiling by nippling up from the branch lines, and at the same time insuring that there will be no unprotected bays by using a staggered sprinkler arrangement.

Tests Under Smooth Ceilings

In order to determine the effect of changes in sprinkler clearance within the range of usual installation practice, a series of fire tests were run under a smooth noncombustible ceiling. In order to maintain uniformity in the test fires, a wood crib fire was used. The crib consisted mainly of 2- by 4-inch pieces of wood with a wide angle spray nozzle beneath discharging gasoline at the rate of 0.73 gallons per minute. The crib was 4 feet square, about 2½ feet high and weighed 300 pounds not counting the 4-by-6 supports. The crib was centered 7 feet below four sprinklers on a 10- by 10-foot spacing. The results of tests, with water supplied to all sprinklers at a flowing pressure of 5 pounds per square inch, are shown in Figures 18, 19, and 20. Other tests were run with increased fire intensities and higher water pressures

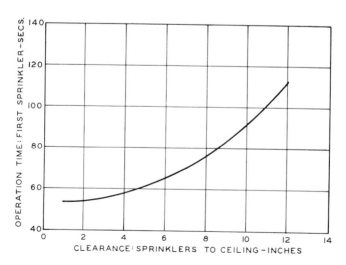

Figure 18. Effect of clearance between ceiling and sprinklers on operating times of sprinklers.

with roughly comparable results, but for the sake of simplicity only the "low" fire tests are shown. It should be kept in mind that the operating times of the sprinklers are much faster than if only common solid combustibles had been used, since the gasoline spray fire produces elevated ceiling temperatures quickly. However, the differences in sprinkler operating times show clearly the effect of changes in clearance between sprinklers and the ceiling.

Figure 18 shows the difference in sprinkler operating times in seconds as the clearance is increased from 1 to 12 inches. In these tests both old-style and standard sprinklers were used and the results plotted together since both types have the same operating time response. As can be seen from an examination of the plotted curve, the operating time increases from about 55 seconds at 2 inches of clearance to about 112 seconds at 12 inches of clearance. Fortunately, the effectiveness of the sprinklers do not change in a proportionate ratio; this is shown by the results in Figures 19 and 20.

Figure 19 shows the results obtained in terms of num bers of sprinklers which operated as the clearance was varied. The same fire exposure was used and the water pres sure was maintained at 5 pounds per square inch. Both old-style and standard sprinklers were installed. It shows a striking difference in the numbers of opened sprinklers especially at the smaller clearances.

With the old-style sprinkler the distribution is continually improved as the clearance is increased, and the number of sprinklers opened decreases rapidly because of the improved distribution until the clearance approaches 10 inches. Beyond this clearance the delay in operation time of the sprinklers more than offsets any benefit from improved distribution so that the number of sprinklers opened rises again for clearances in excess of 10 inches.

With the standard sprinkler, however, there is very little change in distribution as the clearance is varied. At clearances above 6 to 8 inches where there is a substantial increase in operation time of the first sprinkler, the number of opened sprinklers shows a decided increase. This is because the longer the fire burns prior to sprinkler operation the greater the amount of heat developed under the ceiling especially in zones immediately outside of the area over the fire. For this particular type of fire the principal gain in heat development occurs after 1 or 2 minutes from ignition time; this is reflected in the marked upturn in the curve soon afterwards.

Figure 20 is probably the most interesting because it shows to the best advantage the effect of sprinkler discharge on the involved combustibles. Since the exposure of the gasoline spray fire underneath the wood crib is quite constant, the burning of the crib itself is determined primarily by the rate of discharge of sprinkler water on to the upper crib surfaces. More than any other data, these results point out the superior distribution characteristics of the standard sprinkler.

While no continuous weighing of the cribs was attempted during these tests, it appeared that the maximum

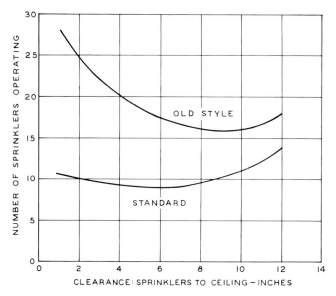

Figure 19. Effect of clearance from ceiling to sprinklers on the number of sprinklers operating.

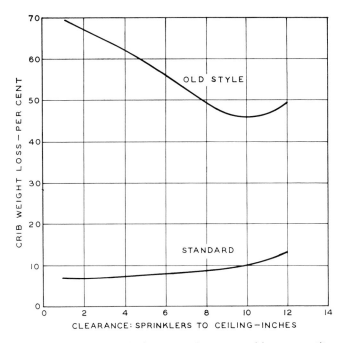

Figure 20. Effect of clearance from sprinklers to ceiling on burning combustibles.

combustion rate of the wood crib took place over a period of 7 to 10 minutes, and that probably 75 per cent of all of the wood combustion occurred during a 10-minute interval. The heat available from the gasoline fire was about 85,000 btu per minute, and the total heat from the 300 pounds of wood would be about 2,400,000 btu assuming complete combustion. Now, if we examine Figure 20 again, we will note that the crib weight loss with old-style sprinklers at 4 inches of clearance was 62 per cent, whereas the loss with standard sprinklers at the same clearance was about 7 per cent. The corresponding heat developments from the wood only would be roughly 1,500,000 btu for 62 per cent and 170,000 btu for 7 per cent. If the maximum sustained heat release per minute for a 5-minute period should be 10 per cent of these figures, then for the old-style sprinkler there would be added to the heat from the gasoline about 150,000 btu per minute for the old-style sprinkler and only about 17,000 btu per minute for the standard sprinkler. The corresponding totals for both wood and gasoline are 235,000 and 102,000 btu per minute respectively. In this connection it is interesting to note from the test data that the maximum 5-minute sustained ceiling temperatures were slightly less than 1,100°F. for the old-style sprinkler at 4 inches of clearance and only about 500°F. for the standard sprinkler at the same clearance.

Additional tests have been made on operating times of sprinklers under panel construction and also under bay-beam construction in order to confirm the applicability of existing sprinkler rules or to provide data which might lead to a proper modification of the rules.

Effect of Beams and Girders

For the panel tests wooden members 14 inches deep divided a smooth ceiling into panels each 10 feet wide by 30 feet long. Sprinklers were spaced 10 feet by 10 feet with three sprinklers per panel with the lines of sprinklers centered at the mid-point in each panel. The sprinkler deflectors were located 4 inches below the beams or 18 inches below the ceiling. The test fires were the same "low" intensity crib fires used in the previous tests. The fires in each case were placed 7 feet below the sprinklers and directly under a beam so as to be centered under four sprinklers. The results of these tests showed operation times about the same as with sprinkler deflectors located 12 inches below a smooth ceiling. The number of sprinklers that operated, the ceiling temperatures, and crib weight losses were also comparable.

For the bay-beam tests, simulated beams 12 inches deep were spaced 10 feet apart and the sprinklers were spaced 10 feet by 10 feet with the deflectors 4 inches below the bottom of the beams. The same test fires were located so as to be centered between two sprinklers and directly under a beam. In these tests the operating times were about the same as with sprinklers located 8 inches below a smooth ceiling. The number of sprinklers opened was about the same as with sprinklers 12 inches below a smooth ceiling, but ceiling temperatures and crib weight losses were somewhat higher.

The general conclusion from these tests, as well as from others along similar lines, is that satisfactory sprinkler protection can be expected for panel and bay-beam construction provided that clearances between sprinklers and ceiling do not substantially exceed those used in these tests. Any significant delay in operation of sprinklers at the limit clearances seems rather small in view of the delay permitted by the sprinkler location rules which are the same for a ceiling 15 feet high or 50 feet high.

chapter 10

PENETRATION THROUGH FIRE DRAFT

In this chapter it will be attempted to show by discussion and a few examples how changes in water pressure and ceiling heights can affect sprinkler protection. At the same time attention will be directed to the danger in assuming that distribution data for sprinklers under "no fire" conditions will be applicable to many fire problems. In addition, it will be made evident that large scale fire test data to show required water density cannot always be safely extrapolated to conditions of large clearances between sprinklers and combustibles, since such tests are usually run in a building of restricted area and with a low to moderate clearance between the ceiling and the fire. A very pertinent example would be tests to determine proper protection for high piled storage of rolled paper in a building high enough to accommodate travelling cranes above the storage. The danger of a faulty conclusion is magnified when it is attempted to obtain the indicated density by increased water pressure.

As the flowing pressure at sprinklers is increased, the water discharge rate is increased in proportion to the square root of the pressure. When the distribution of a sprinkler is measured by means of collecting pans at varied distances below the sprinklers, increased discharge densities are found with increasing water pressure and at the same time the distribution pattern is modified by a gain in the lateral throw of water spray. While such distribution tests have been made at widely varying clearances between the sprinklers and the collecting pans, it was assumed that the measurements under "no fire" conditions would not be changed substantially with a fire in progress under the sprinklers. This assumption has been proved to be far from correct, based on controlled tests with variances in both clearances and fire intensity.

Effect of Pressure and Clearance Between Sprinklers and Combustibles on Sprinkler Spray Penetration

An example of the effect of fire draft (and clearance) on the penetration of sprinkler water spray through a moderate-sized fire is given in the results of a series of tests in which the water penetration was measured in a 10-square-foot pan located just below a small wide angle spray nozzle discharging 1.5 gallons per minute of burning gasoline. With standard sprinklers on a 10- by 10-foot spacing and located 5 feet above this gasoline fire, the percentage of water collected in the pan as compared to "no fire" conditions was 65 at 10 pounds per square inch, 52 at 25 pounds per square inch, 41 at 50 pounds per square inch and 32 at 100 pounds per square inch. When the clearance between the sprinklers and the pan was increased to 29 feet, the corresponding figures were 38, 33, 27 and 17.

These results are shown graphically in Figure 21. This shows quite clearly the effect of the change in clearance between the fire and the sprinklers as well as the effect of pressure. Even though there is a steady decrease in the percentages with increased pressure, there is an actual gain in the "amount" of water reaching the pan because of the increased sprinkler flow rate. With a severe fire, particularly at the greater clearance, the amount of water reaching the pan might be decreased, especially in the higher pressure ranges.

Effect of High Water Pressure

To show the effect of increased water atomization without changing sprinkler discharge rate or clearance between sprinklers and combustibles, a pair of tests were run using standard automatic sprinklers on a 10- by 10-foot spacing over a fire in a wood crib consisting mostly of two by fours, 4 feet square by $3\frac{1}{2}$ feet high, and weighing approximately 400 pounds. No gasoline spray was used. The top of the crib was centered $7\frac{1}{2}$ feet below four sprinklers. In one test $\frac{1}{2}$-inch orifice sprinklers were installed and operated at 5 pounds per square inch to discharge 12.8 gallons per

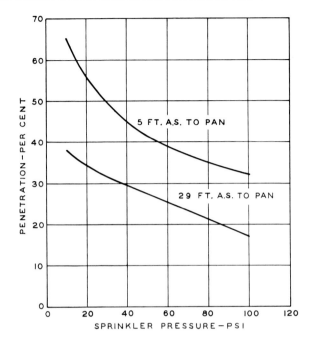

Figure 21. Effect of clearances and water pressure on sprinkler discharge penetration.

minute. In the other test the sprinklers installed had reduced orifices (to about 5/16 inch diameter) so that it required 61 pounds per square inch to give the same flow rate of 12.8 gallons per minute. The distribution density patterns were approximately the same under "no fire" conditions although it was obvious that the reduced orifice sprinklers had a much greater atomization of the spray discharge.

With the ½-inch orifice sprinklers operating at 5 pounds per square inch pressure, the weight loss from the crib was only 10 per cent, and six sprinklers opened. With the small orifice sprinklers operating at 61 pounds per square inch pressure, the water breakup was vastly improved, but the crib weight loss jumped to 62 per cent and the number of sprinklers that opened increased to nine.

From the appearance of the fire, it seemed that very little water actually reached the crib. It was obvious that the very fine spray could not effectively penetrate down through the fire draft, and the resulting increased fire intensity affected a greater ceiling area in spite of better cooling at high levels from the high pressure discharge.

From the foregoing example and its discussion one might assume that increased pressure resulting in finer water breakup would be detrimental. Fortunately, in the usual water supply pressure range for multiple sprinkler operation (about 5 pounds per square inch to 40 pounds per square inch), the degree of atomization does not approach that which occurred with the example of a reduced orifice and 61 pounds per square inch pressure. With standard ½-inch orifice sprinklers in the normal water pressure range, more water reaches the combustibles even though the percentage of the discharge reaching the combustibles is reduced as the pressure is increased. While this statement is true for most ordinary conditions, the water reaching the combustibles and the degree of protection may suffer with very severe fire conditions or with large clearances between the sprinklers and combustibles — particularly clearances greater than 12 feet to 15 feet. Under these conditions it is best to obtain the required density by using relatively low pressures with the sprinklers more closely spaced.

Effect of Clearance at Two Moderate Pressures

To test the effect of changing clearance between standard sprinklers and ordinary combustibles, a series of fires were run in single stacks of 4-foot-square standard hardwood pallets 8 feet high centered under four sprinklers on a 10- by 10-foot spacing. These tests were run in sprinklered areas large enough so that the maximum number of sprinklers which could be opened would be observed. The clearance between sprinklers and combustibles was varied by changing the elevation of the stack which was kept constant in its size, form, and moisture content. The tests were run at two pressures, 19 pounds per square inch and 40 pounds

Factory Mutual Engineering Division

Figure 22.   Test fire in 8-foot-high stack of pallets mounted above the floor to permit changing the clearance between the stack and sprinklers.

per square inch, from which the average calculated water discharge densities under "no fire" conditions would be 0.25 and 0.36 gallons per minute per square foot.

Figure 23 shows the results of the tests at four clearances, namely 18 inches, 36 inches, 7 feet and 16½ feet. Since it is believed that the loss in weight by combustion in the pallet stacks is the best measure of any deficiency in direct wetting, the pallets were weighed before the test and after a fixed burning time were dried and weighed again. At 19 pounds per square inch water pressure on the sprinklers, the stack weight losses were 177, 163, 290, and 320 pounds at 1½, 3, 7, and 16½ feet respectively; the number of sprinklers opened were correspondingly 10, 18, 19, and

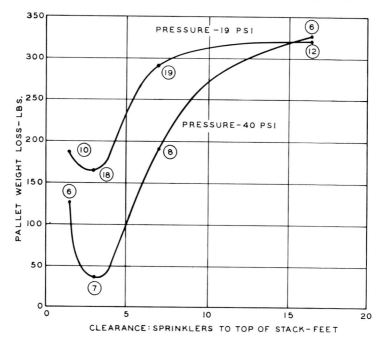

Figure 23. Effect of clearances on extinguishing efficiency
and number of sprinklers operating. (Note: Figures in the circles
are the number of sprinklers that opened.)

12. At 40 pounds per square inch water pressure the weight
losses were 126, 36, 190, 325 pounds, and the number of
sprinklers opened were 6, 7, 8, and 6 respectively.

It is interesting to note that at 16½ feet clearance the
pallet stack was no better protected at the higher pressure,
although the number of sprinklers opened was less at all
clearances due to the superior cooling effect at levels near
the ceiling. Even though these test fires were relatively
small, the finer water drops from the higher pressure discharge, at the 16½-foot clearance, were even further reduced
in size by evaporation in the longer travel distance, and were
thus unable to penetrate the fire draft and reach the pallets
to any greater degree than the coarser drops obtained at
lower pressures and discharge rates. With a more severe

fire, the comparison in pallet weight loss would be even less favorable to the higher pressure discharge at the maximum clearance.

Assuming that sprinkler water distribution on to the top of the pallet stacks is inversely proportional to the pallet weight loss by combustion, these results confirm the general advice to the effect that not less than 3 feet clearance should be allowed for the protection of closely packed high piled stock. At the same time it is puzzling, at least prior to careful analysis, to explain why there were 10 sprinklers opened at a pressure of 19 pounds per square inch and at a clearance of 18 inches as compared to 18 sprinklers at the same pressure and 3 feet clearance. In the latter set of circumstances, the distribution of water on to the top of the stack should have been better with a lesser number of sprinklers opened instead of more. The only explanation appears to be that at the smaller clearance (18 inches) the escape of partially inert products of combustion was prevented in some degree so that the fire intensity was reduced. However, because of the poorer distribution the fire burned longer prior to any effective control so that the pallet weight loss was a little higher at the 18-inch clearance. In the case of the tests at these two low clearances at the 40 pounds per square inch pressure, the numbers of sprinklers that opened were almost the same, undoubtedly because the cooling effect on the atmosphere around the sprinklers was so great, regardless of some differences in distribution of water on to the pallet fires.

While the results obtained in these tests would not necessarily be duplicated with other types of fires and at other fire intensities, they do indicate, at least for small- to moderate-sized fires in ordinary combustibles, that the most favorable clearances are in the range of 2 to 5 or 6 feet. The results also show that with large clearances between sprinklers and combustibles, high water pressures are of somewhat dubious advantage in control and extinguishment of fire, although the numbers of sprinklers opened were kept to relatively small figures. However, in combustible storage in larger masses, if the fire control is poor, the fire will spread and continue to spread so that eventually large numbers of sprinklers will open.

For a fire hazard in ordinary combustibles where a sprinkler water density over .25 gallons per minute per square foot is required for effective fire control and where clearances between sprinklers and combustibles is in excess of about 12 feet, the use of standard ½-inch orifice sprinklers at the low pressure needed to produce the required coarse discharge may not be economically practicable. A considerable gain in density can be obtained by the use of approved large-orifice standard sprinklers which discharge 40 per cent more water than the ½-inch orifice sprinkler at the same water pressure but with no more water breakup. These large-orifice sprinklers screw directly into ¾-inch fittings and must be fed through special-sized pipe.

For high piled storage such as bulky stock (rolled paper or appliances in wood or paperboard cartons) piled well over 20 feet in height and with clearances in excess of about 12 feet, reliable protection may not always be assured even with the use of large-orifice sprinklers on a reduced spacing. These conditions are often met where the storage is handled by overhead cranes. For such extremely hazardous circumstances, subdivision of values is indicated to reduce the possibility of large single loss, and the storage area should be under very strict control with respect to any possible ignition hazards.

chapter 11

PROTECTION AGAINST SEVERE EXPOSURE

Occasionally the fire protection engineer is confronted with the problem of determining the most practical and effective protection system for an extra hazardous process carried on inside a building. An example is solvent extraction and recovery processes located in high steel frame structures with tanks of volatile flammable liquids supported on steel work at various elevations. Some of these buildings are 100 feet in height and areas may run to 3,000 square feet or more. A great deal of experimenting and large scale testing had been done to adapt water spray nozzles to this service but little information was available on the capacity and limitations of automatic sprinklers when used in the same service. In the hope that a simpler and possibly more economical system than spray nozzle protection could be developed, a test program was formulated, a special steel skeleton structure was erected, and a series of tests were run at the Factory Mutual Engineering Division laboratory. A strong influence in deciding on this program was the experience showing the limitations on sprinkler effectiveness imposed by the combination of high water pressures and substantial clearances between sprinklers and ordinary combustibles.

Test Conditions and Results

The structure for these tests was a skeleton steel frame erected in a 40- by 60-foot area with 33 feet of headroom. The steelwork had a heavy vertical H-column and 8-inch I-beam crossarms at the floor, at the 10-foot level and at the 20-foot level. The crossarms were fastened to the central H-column, and were located around the column 90 degrees apart. In each of the floor quadrants there was provided a

Factory Mutual Engineering Division

Figure 24. I-beam test structure used to determine action of sprinklers in protection of exposed steel against severe flammable liquid fire.

spray nozzle supplied with gasoline under pump pressure so that the four nozzles discharged a total of 9.5 gallons per minute. Thermocouples were located at frequent intervals along the H-column and the crossarms to show steel temperatures. Other thermocouples were located 8 inches under the ceiling to show air temperatures.

The total heat generated by these gasoline fires was about 1,100,000 btu per minute. The flames completely surrounded the central column and extended about 20 feet above the gasoline nozzles. To supply air for the combustion of the gasoline, two roof hatches were opened (about 56 square feet) and building doors were also opened. To evaluate the degree of protection obtained with different sprinkler arrangements, multiple point recorders were employed to print all of the thermocouple readings. To simplify the reporting of results, only the maximum temperatures recorded at the H-column and at the crossarms are given in the following discussion.

The sprinkler systems installed for these tests consisted of 14 sprinklers at the ceiling on 7- by 7-foot spacing, eight sprinklers at the ceiling on 10- by 10-foot spacing, four sprinklers on 10- by 10-foot spacing under the crossarms at the 18½-foot level, and four sprinklers on 10- by 10-foot spacing at the 8½-foot level. Standard 165°F. sprinklers were used.

In one of the early tests with ceiling sprinklers only, the eight sprinklers on 10- by 10-foot spacing were operated at 40 gallons per minute per sprinkler. As might be expected with this water density and the greater water break-up at the high pressure required, the protection was not good; the maximum column temperature was 1,290°F., the maximum crossarm temperature 1,495°F., and the maximum ceiling temperature 455°F.

In another test with ceiling sprinklers only, the 14 sprinklers on 7- by 7-foot spacing were used. They were supplied with water at the rate of 30 gallons per minute per sprinkler to give an average density of 0.60 gallons per minute per square foot. During this test of 20 minutes duration the maximum column temperature was 565°F., the maximum crossarm temperature reached 1,160°F., but the ceiling temperature reached only 210°F.

In a third test the protection consisted of eight ceiling sprinklers on 10- by 10-foot spacing, four sprinklers on 10- by 10-foot spacing at the 18½-foot level, and the same layout at the 8½-foot level, all operated at 20 gallons per minute per sprinkler to give an overall density of 0.60 gallons per minute per square foot. In this test the maximum column temperature was 300°F., the maximum crossarm temperature was 695°F., and the maximum ceiling air temperature was 370°F.

A fourth test was run with only the sprinklers in operation at the 8½- and 18½-foot levels, but the flowing pressure was increased to 30 gallons per minute per sprinkler. The average density was 0.60 gallons per minute per square foot but the piping arrangement was simplified. The results of this test showed a maximum column temperature of 230°F., a maximum crossarm temperature of 260°F., and a maximum ceiling air temperature of only 380°F., in spite of the lack of ceiling sprinklers.

Discussion of Test Results

A comparison of the first two tests shows a very decided advantage in favor of the closer sprinkler spacing. The average overall distribution density in the first test was 0.40 gallons per minute per square foot compared with 0.60 gallons per minute per square foot in the second test. However, the difference in temperatures for the steelwork cannot be explained solely on the basis of the increased discharge density in the second test, but must have been due in some measure to the ability of the large water drops at the lower pressure to penetrate down through the strong fire draft. Even so, the margin of safety in protection of the steel column in the second test was not generous, and the temperature of the crossarms was high enough so that structural failure could be expected with any normal loading of the crossarms.

In the tests with sprinklers under the steel crossarms at intermediate levels (the third and fourth tests) the protection in both cases was much improved although not quite good enough at 20 gallons per minute per sprinkler even with sprinklers operating at the ceiling. However, at 30 gallons per minute per sprinkler at the 8½- and 18½-foot levels the protection was excellent, and ceiling air temperatures were kept down satisfactorily even with no ceiling sprinklers.

These tests show that the effective range of sprinklers in protecting against severe hazards is probably no greater than 10 to 12 feet, and for best results even less. This is shown by some of the detailed temperature results of the second test with 14 standard sprinklers at the ceiling on 7- by 7-foot spacing and operating at 30 gallons per minute per sprinkler. These results showed average crossarm temperatures at the 20-foot level (12 feet below the sprinklers) to be 500°F. lower than average crossarm temperatures at the 10-foot level (22 feet below the sprinklers).

It was also demonstrated in a repeat of the second test with no more interference to water distribution than would be produced by an upright 50-gallon drum resting in the vertical position on one of the upper crossarms that the crossarm temperature under the drum ran about 300°F. higher than without this low order interference. The conclusion is that additional sprinklers or spray nozzles must be located to protect the bottoms of tanks or other equipment and supporting steelwork.

Protection by Directed Spray

During the course of this investigation into the value of sprinklers against severe exposure one of the members of the Factory Mutual laboratory staff, Mr. Malcolm H. Nickerson, suggested that, instead of attempting to force sprinkler water downward against the fire draft, advantage might be taken of the air flow into the fire to carry fine water spray with it. Accordingly, tests were run with spray nozzles of varying angles and capacities. A number of locations and arrangements of nozzles were tried, generally with fairly high flowing pressures in order to get a high degree of atomization. The same exposure fire was used as was the same steel structure already described.

Since a fire of this magnitude and flame height draws in air for combustion not only at and near floor level but also at elevations as high as the flame, the ideal arrangement appeared to call for multiple nozzles at two or three elevations and directed into the flaming volume from points surrounding the fire. However, it was desired to keep a simple and economical piping layout and to place nozzles at a sufficient distance from the floor so as not to interfere with normal traffic. At the same time it was realized that any discharge from the nozzles which actually impinged on to the floor would be wasted. After several trials it seemed that a nozzle elevation of 9 feet would be effective.

The most favorable arrangement, from the standpoint of effectiveness, simplicity, and economy, made use of four ⅜-inch diameter spray nozzles discharging in the form of a "solid" cone of about 130 degrees included angle. These

Factory Mutual Engineering Division

Figure 25. Test fire involving 50-gallon drums mounted on crossarms of the I-beam test structure and the operation of only ceiling sprinklers. Test showed the need for additional sprinklers or spray nozzles to protect supporting steel work.

nozzles were placed so that each nozzle discharged from the center of each side of a rectangular loop approximately 20 feet square. The nozzles were aimed to discharge horizontally into the fire, and at the 9-foot elevation practically no water was discharged on to the floor. The best result was obtained at 100 pounds per square inch flowing pressure which gave a water discharge rate per nozzle of 29 gallons per minute or 116 gallons per minute for all four nozzles. At an initial water temperature of 60°F., the discharge from the four nozzles was capable, upon complete vaporization at 212°F., of absorbing, theoretically, the heat from the combustion of 9.5 gallons per minute of gasoline. However, no such heat absorbing efficiency was expected with such a simple nozzle arrangement which could not possibly distribute water spray throughout the active combustion zone. Nevertheless, it was hoped that the forward motion of the 130 degree angle spray would carry the water into the fire, and that the high pressure would break up the water drops so finely that they would in turn be carried upward through the combustion zone so as to produce an effective cooling and oxygen dilution action.

The results of the test with this arrangement gave a maximum column temperature of 145°F. as compared with 230°F. for the best sprinkler arrangement, a maximum crossarm temperature of 265°F. compared with 260°F. for the sprinklers, and a maximum ceiling temperature of 375°F., actually 5°F. less than the sprinklers. Accordingly, the protection with the spray nozzles was judged to be at least as good as with the sprinklers, and probably a little better. Since the sprinklers at 30 gallons per minute per sprinkler required a total of 240 gallons per minute and the spray nozzles a total of 116 gallons per minute, the latter appeared to be twice as efficient per gallon of water used. One serious disadvantage of the spray nozzle scheme is the high water pressure required which is not always available. While not tested, it is believed that as good results could be obtained with eight or more smaller nozzles which could be operated at more moderate pressures and with better spray distribution.

chapter 12

WATER SUPPLY TO SPRINKLERS

The principal factors which govern the selection of proper water supply to sprinklers are the expected fire intensity from the occupancy (and construction) and the probable number of sprinklers which might open. The expected fire intensity will determine the allowable spacing of sprinklers and the pressure of the water supply at the sprinklers. The volume rate of the water supply (total gallons per minute) which should be available will in turn depend on the maximum number of sprinklers which may open and the average rate of flow from each sprinkler. Any change in the nature or arrangement of the occupancy may increase the hazard — sometimes to a degree which will make the protection inadequate.

Ordinary Hazards

The water pressure at which a sprinkler operates, whether by itself or in combination with others, is governed by the water supply to the sprinkler system, by the size of pipes between sprinkler lines and between sprinklers on branch lines, and by the length of pipe both between lines and between sprinklers. Schedules of pipe sizes are chosen generally to give a pressure sufficient for adequate fire control in ordinary construction and occupancy in view of the maximum number of sprinklers which might be expected to open, based on experience for the construction and occupancy. A 5 pounds per square inch flowing pressure on the most remote or next to most remote sprinkler, considering the probability of opening many sprinklers in the area, is generally considered sufficient for an ordinary combustible occupancy. Water supply rules have been developed for various ordinary occupancies and areas to provide such a flowing pressure, allowing for the head pressure loss in risers and for flowing friction loss in the sprinkler risers, cross mains and piping. It is also usual to provide some additional water supply capacity from the same source because of probable use of hose streams.

Extra Hazards

Water supplies for occupancies with hazards greater than ordinary, such as high-piled stock in warehouses or those involving flammable liquids, require increased sprinkler discharge densities and sometimes higher flowing pressures than those supplied to ordinary occupancies. Some of this increased protection can be obtained by stronger water supplies, some by a decreased protected area per sprinkler, and in some instances by increasing pipe sizes in the entire sprinkler system. Whereas average water densities around the order of 0.12 to 0.15 gallons per minute per square foot may be sufficient for ordinary hazard occupancies, extra hazardous occupancies may require densities of 0.30 gallons per minute per square foot or even up to 0.60 gallons per minute per square foot or more. In some instances, large scale tire storage for example, the fire may persist for long periods during which smoke prevents effective manual fire fighting. In such cases, the availability of the water supply over long periods becomes quite important.

Light Hazards

Water supplies for light hazard occupancies (less than ordinary) are usually calculated for the same sprinkler flowing pressures required for ordinary occupancies but a lesser total rate of water flow is allowed. The lesser protection which it is assumed will be required is adjusted by allowing a greater area per sprinkler (up to 200 square feet). In developing rules for light hazard water supplies, consideration has been given to the division of buildings into small areas by partitions, even if the partitions do not qualify as good fire cutoffs.

In allowing up to 200 square feet per sprinkler for protection in a light hazard occupancy, the distribution characteristics of the standard sprinkler should not be ignored. In the first place, the sprinklers were designed to give complete coverage at an elevation 4 feet below the sprinklers when spaced 10 feet by 10 feet on lines and when the discharge rate was 15 gallons per minute per sprinkler. However, when sprinklers are spaced 14 feet by 14 feet on lines allowing 196 square feet of coverage per sprinkler, there is an area of about 16 square feet at 4 feet below the sprinklers which receives practically no water when the sprinkler flow rate is 15 gallons per minute. At discharge rates higher than 15 gallons per minute the lateral throw of the sprinkler discharge is increased which in turn increases the area covered. Thus if the flowing pressure is increased to 30 gallons per minute per sprinkler, the unprotected area at the 4-foot level below each sprinkler is reduced to about 5 square feet. At elevations closer than 4 feet below the sprinkler or when discharge rates are less than 15 gallons per minute, the unprotected area may be seriously increased.

While the effective operation of sprinklers is important regardless of the degree of hazard, the elimination of obstructions to sprinkler distribution becomes of prime importance when attempts are made to reduce the number of sprinklers installed by locating them at the widest allowable spacing.

Hazard Somewhat Uncertain

While the degree of hazard of the occupancy (expected fire intensity) will govern the water discharge density to be supplied, it does not necessarily follow that a low fire hazard from the intensity standpoint will require only a small volume of water. For example, the heat release per square foot of floor area or fire intensity for some occupancies containing textile fibers may be relatively low. However, fire may spread over loose surfaces at a rapid rate well ahead of the operation of sprinklers, resulting in a large fire-involved area and in a large number of opened sprinklers. The rate of combustion per unit area (fire intensity) after the first rapid lateral travel spread may be so low that a minimum sprinkler discharge density is sufficient to extinguish the fire. For this type of hazard, while the water supply volume rate may need to be generous, the sprinkler spacing can be increased to a value above average. A parallel example might be the accidental spillage of 5 to 10 gallons of gasoline in an occupancy otherwise of low combustibility. The short duration flash fire will open large numbers of sprinklers with little or no effect on the gasoline fire, after which the sprinkler discharge density need be only of an order required by the general occupancy.

The textile fiber occupancy is a good example of what may result if fire should spread ahead of sprinkler operation. However, somewhat similar effects may result from other factors with occupancies where ordinary rapid lateral fire spread would not be expected. Any conditions which would cause excessive delay in the operation of sprinklers might require larger water supply volume rates than normal. Probably the most common of these conditions is excessive clearance above combustibles, which may prevail in some storage areas.

chapter 13

BUILDING CONSTRUCTION
AND SPRINKLER PROTECTION

When important and valuable buildings have truly noncombustible construction and contain an occupancy which is not only noncombustible but can be relied upon to stay so, it is obvious that sprinkler protection is not needed. It is also obvious that sprinklers should be installed in properties when both construction and occupancy are combustible. Where other combinations exist in varying degrees of combustibility, it is sometimes difficult to say just how strong the protection should be, or in some cases whether it is needed at all.

Roofs of Low Combustibility

There are certain types of insulated steel deck construction with no vapor seal or with a vapor seal tested and approved from the standpoint of combustibility which, in the view of some, may not require sprinkler protection provided the occupancy is safe enough from fire hazard so that it would not normally need sprinklers. These constructions are not noncombustible; they merely have a sufficiently low combustibility to prevent a continuously spreading fire when subjected only to a moderately low exposure around the order of magnitude of a fire in two adjacent 8-foot-high stacks of 4-foot-square standard slatted hardwood pallets.

Common Wood Roof Construction

It is not generally appreciated how resistant to ignition are common wood roof constructions of average moisture content. Experiments have been made to ignite a joisted wood ceiling of 2- by 12-inch joists spaced 16 inches apart on centers. The ceiling itself over the joists was of matched nominal 1-inch thick boards, and the moisture content of the joists and boards was approximately 15 per cent. Igniters used in the tests were two closely spaced wads of compact cellulose fiber each 3 inches in diameter and 5 inches long, and each soaked with about 4 ounces of gasoline. These igniters provide a strong local ignition source for a period exceeding 7 minutes. The igniters were placed up against the board ceiling and fastened alongside of the joists. After lighting, the igniters burned vigorously and the ceiling construction ignited in turn with the flaming spreading along the joist channel for a distance of 5 or 6 feet. However, even though the igniters were still burning strongly, the flames spread no further in the construction, and after the igniters had burned out, the fire in the ceiling construction went out.

In another test a 3-inch-thick tongue and groove fir plank roof was installed supported on protected steel beams on the Factory Mutual roof deck testing structure which has overall dimensions of 20 feet by 100 feet. The exposure fire was from a gasoline spray partially premixed with air at one end of the structure. Ample additional air was supplied by a blower to complete combustion and to allow air for burning of the roof. The exposure was such as to duplicate in the first 20- by 20-foot bay of the structure the standard ASTM temperature-time curve for testing fire resistance of building assemblies. Within 4 or 5 minutes after ignition of the gasoline the wood roof in the first bay was flaming, and the flaming was allowed to spread to almost 60 feet from the firing end at which time the exposure was abruptly cut off. The flaming at the roof quickly subsided, and within a few minutes active combustion had ceased except for some minor residual glowing close to the firing end. In this instance, the roof planks had been conditioned to an average moisture content of about 13 per cent.

From the tests with both the joisted ceiling and the plank roof, one might assume that wood construction is difficult to ignite, except very locally. This may be true with wood moisture contents up around 15 per cent, which could occur in warm weather periods of relatively high atmospheric humidity. However, moisture contents in heated buildings in the cold weather may drop to as low as 5 to 8 per cent. Under the latter conditions, ignition of wood construction to produce spreading fires is much more likely to take place.

Regardless of the difficulties encountered in obtaining spreading ignition under certain test conditions, there has been enough actual fire experience in buildings of combustible construction containing a normally noncombustible occupancy to warrant the installation of automatic sprinklers whenever a building and its contents have a substantial value. An exception might be made in the case of a building of moderate area with a plank on steel beam roof housing only steel or other noncombustible stock and with an automatic fire alarm system installed and a public fire department nearby.

Occupancy — the Sole Criterion?

Over a period of several years at the Factory Mutual laboratories test station a large number of fire tests (with standard sprinklers on 10- by 10-foot spacing) have been made with various degrees of occupancy hazard and with combustible ceilings of wood, either as boards on joists or as double matched boards on wood beams with the beams at various spacings from 5 to 10 feet. In no case, regardless of the occupancy fire, was there the slightest difficulty in extinguishing the ceiling fire provided the protection was sufficient to control the occupancy fire. In some instances, when the sprinkler protection was shut off as soon as the occupancy fire was under control, there was residual glowing in cracks between ceiling boards. Such residual glowing once established would have continued for a while even if higher sprinkler discharge densities had been employed. As a result of this long experience, we were forced to a tentative conclusion at least that if the protection is adequate for the occupancy there need be no concern about the safety of combustible construction, provided the sprinklers are placed with due regard to clearance below the ceiling or roof obstructions to distribution are avoided, and sprinklers are staggered on alternate lines where necessary to prevent undue delay in sprinkler operation and to prevent the existence of unprotected bay channels. How far it is proper to go on allotted area per sprinkler has not been fully determined; the present approved standard sprinkler which was designed originally for a protected area of 100 square feet or somewhat more at a distance of 4 feet below the sprinklers is a case in point.

The foregoing test examples and the discussion and tentative conclusions were all based on the most favorable conditions of strength of protection with respect to the occupancy, no interruption of protection, no failure of any sprinkler, no interference to sprinkler distribution, no clogged sprinkler lines, and no other deficiencies in the installation and maintenance of the systems.

Combustible Construction Adds to Occupancy Hazard

When large increments are added to the area to be protected per sprinkler, there are many factors which need to be considered very carefully, particularly when the construction is combustible. The further apart sprinklers are spaced, the more necessary it becomes to properly classify the occupancy, whether light, ordinary, or extra hazard, because the margin of safety available is much reduced if not eliminated. If the occupancy or some significant portion of it should be increased in hazard over that existing when the sprinkler installation was made, the margin of safety is not only lost, but it is quite likely that the protection may be inadequate.

With ceilings of combustible construction, the potential heat contribution rate depends generally upon the surface area of the exposed construction and on its accessibility to some air supply. In open joisted construction the exposed area is relatively large, and, since combustion gases can flow away readily through the joist channels, there is no tendency to confine products of combustion with their lowered oxygen content which would decrease the burning rate of the construction. The condition is much the same in the case of plank on wood or steel beams, except that the exposed surface area of the combustible construction is substantially reduced. If the wood joists are framed into the beams or otherwise fire stopped at moderate intervals, or if in the case of plank and beam construction the beams are framed into girders to form panels, the escape of products of combustion is very much slowed down, and the oxygen-deficient atmosphere is retained in the channels or panels so that the combustion rate is also slowed down.

For most situations involving what we refer to as "ordinary" occupancy, the distribution density from standard sprinklers with a good water supply, even at coverages up to 130 square feet per sprinkler, is quite adequate to control a fire in the combustibles below, so that the combustibility of the ceiling is not the predominant factor. However, with a weak water supply, or a somewhat greater than ordinary hazard such a high-piled stock or with some special hazard introduced into the occupancy, the combustible ceiling would then become involved, resulting in the opening of a larger number of sprinklers with a corresponding reduction in the sprinkler discharge density. On the other hand, if the ceiling were noncombustible, the fire would remain localized except for the usual relatively slow lateral travel through the combustible occupancy.

With any deficiency or impairment in the sprinkler protection there is no question but that a ceiling or roof of combustible construction will add more to the total heat in a fire than one of noncombustible construction. Furthermore, an intermediate floor of boards on joist would have less resistance against burn-through than a noncombustible floor, or even one of plank on beam construction, which usually has a hardwood overlay. In passing, it might also be noted that the resistance against collapse of roofs supported on modern very light bar joists is not even as good as board on joist roofs, especially if the latter are framed into beams or otherwise fire stopped. Consequently, for combustible construction, particularly light construction, it would appear advisable to consider some extra protection features over that which would be recommended for noncombustible or heavy construction.

The argument has been proposed that combustible construction should have closer sprinkler spacing, because, if protection should be temporarily impaired, a fire from a local exposure would open many more sprinklers than in the case of a noncombustible ceiling. This argument is not well based; such an unfortunate circumstance would call for a stronger water supply rather than reduced sprinkler spacing. On the other hand, in some cases, closer sprinkler spacing might be a good idea in view of the possibility of defective sprinklers or the more likely interference with good distribution from obstructions such as ventilating ducts, light fixtures, etc. With the control exercised in the manufacture of the modern standard automatic sprinkler, failure of a sprinkler to open is an extremely rare occurrence, especially in the temperature rating range from 135°F. to 250°F. While there is a chance of linkage parts lodging on the deflector in such a manner as to adversely affect the distribution of water, there is a much greater chance of spoiling distribution by locating sprinklers too close to structural members such as steel truss or steel beams, or improperly with respect to fixtures and equipment. The current sprinkler rules are good in their prohibition of poor practice affecting sprinkler distribution; these rules should be followed very carefully, especially at the wider sprinkler spacings now tolerated.

chapter 14

COMMENTS ON THE NFPA SPRINKLER STANDARD

Editor's Note: The discussion in this chapter of the NFPA Standard for the Installation of Sprinkler Systems (NFPA No. 13) is based on the 1963 edition of that Standard.

No comprehensive discussion or detailed examination of the sprinkler rules is intended in this chapter; rather it is proposed to deal with certain sections of the rules which in the author's opinion need some explanation or clarification, and in a few instances possibly some modification.

The sprinkler rules, published by the National Fire Protection Association as Standard for the Installation of Sprinkler Systems (NFPA No. 13), have had a long and complicated history. The rules had their beginning in the latter part of the nineteenth century when industrial roof and floor constructions were largely confined to wood joist and plank on timber. When first printed in 1896, the Sprinkler Standard concerned itself principally with sprinkler pipe sizes, sprinkler spacing, and water supplies. Since 1900 the Sprinkler Standard has been subject to considerable amplification and refinement. New types of construction have come into vogue; among them are planks on steel beams and planks on steel truss or purlins supported by beams or trusses. At the same time, roof decks of gypsum slab or concrete slab have replaced some of the plank decks, and, more recently, roof decks have been made of insulated steel supported on very light steel truss designated as bar joist. Concurrent with some of these developments heavy construction was introduced in the form of reinforced concrete supported on "mushroom" columns or on fireproofed steel columns.

Over the years other new developments such as extensive ventilation and air conditioning systems, new lighting fixtures, and process equipment attached to or located close to ceilings have combined with some of the new structural elements to impose serious threats to good sprinkler water distribution. In addition, flammable liquids and other hazardous materials were introduced into industrial processes. Furthermore, in order to speed up and to economize in manufacturing and assembly operations conveyor production lines were installed, in many cases necessitating the removal of fire walls, resulting in larger areas subject to a single fire loss. As lift trucks and overhead traveling cranes became available, finished stock and raw materials were piled to heights unheard of in 1900, with an attendant increase in the fire hazard.

The changes in building construction, equipment, and occupancy mentioned in the preceding paragraphs together with many others not listed have caused an almost continuous review of the Sprinkler Standard and periodic revision of its rules. There have also been many additions to take care of special construction details. A few of these have been prompted by a desire to bring about some saving in the cost of sprinkler installations. The overall effect of all of these changes has been to develop a Sprinkler Standard which in length and complexity goes far beyond that which was considered adequate 40 years ago when sprinkler installations in industrial properties were quite commonplace.

It seems entirely possible that the Sprinkler Standard could be simplified and that many of its rules applying to special structural conditions could be eliminated. The project would require a searching study into the fundamental factors involved — particularly the objectives and purposes of the variants in the rules. For example, one question that should be considered is: Are we still trying to protect the ceiling construction, or are we satisfied that adequate protection for the occupancy will also be good enough for the construction whether combustible or noncombustible?

One repetitious detail in the rules has to do with the maximum distance at which a sprinkler may be located below the ceiling or roof deck. The limitation obviously has to do with toleration of time delay in sprinkler operation and to some extent protection of the ceiling construction. The prime purpose of the distance limitation must be to cut down time delay because there is a much greater difference in allowable distance with different types of construction than is imposed because the deck is combustible instead of noncombustible. Time delay in sprinkler water discharge can be caused by the time required to expel the air from a dry-pipe sprinkler system, by the use of sprinklers of temperature ratings above ordinary, by the distance a sprinkler is located below the ceiling, by the allowable sprinkler spacing, and, most importantly, by marked changes in the distance between the sprinklers and the combustible occupancy below. So we are faced with the heart of the problem — to determine how much time delay in sprinkler operation is tolerable and what difference it does make whether the construction is combustible or not. In view of all of the other factors affecting time delay in sprinkler operation, it is suspected that the differential between combustible and noncombustible construction can be eliminated without seriously impairing the fire protection. Certainly the delay in operation because of high ceilings is much greater than would result by placing a sprinkler deflector 12 inches below the ceiling rather than 10 inches below.

Sprinkler System Failures

The experience with sprinkler protection over the years has been remarkably good, and, where failures have occurred, there has practically always been a good reason. Some of these reasons may be listed as follows:

1. Incomplete sprinkler protection
2. Occupancy hazard improperly assessed
3. Weak water supply — inadequate pressure or volume
4. Obstruction of sprinkler discharge distribution
5. Abnormally high ceilings
6. Change of occupancy — general or local
7. Sprinklers shut off before fire (closed valves)

8. Sprinklers shut off too soon
9. Sprinkler piping clogged — scale or other foreign material
10. System out of service on account of freezing
11. Piping or fittings broken — inadequate support, explosions, mechanical injury.

Of these various reasons only the first five are factors in the original installation of the sprinkler system, although occasionally Number 11 can be anticipated and guarded against. Under the current sprinkler rules there may be added, under some conditions, inadequate protection because of excessive area allowance per sprinkler, but this is only a subdivision of reason Number 1.

In regard to incomplete sprinkler protection, some of the more common omissions are:

Halls and stairways in hotels, hospitals, schools, and other such buildings because of presumed lack of combustibles in these areas. However, in the event of fire in any of the connecting rooms, the chances of successful escape are very much improved by sprinkler protection which tends to wash and cool the atmosphere. The danger from toxic and irritating gases is considerably increased with higher atmosphere temperatures.

Spaces above false ceilings and under wooden first floors, especially if there are any combustibles in these spaces and if there are any chances of ignition, either within the space or entering from the exterior.

Large exhaust stacks, ventilating ducts, chambers in air conditioning systems, dust collecting bins and filters, conveyor enclosures, laundry and delivery chutes, and paint spray booths.

Dryers and drying ovens with either combustible construction or contents.

Under cutting tables, mezzanine floors, and offices with their own ceilings under the main sprinklered ceiling.

High storage multitier racks and shelving especially over 4 feet wide where intermediate level sprinklers should be installed.

Office partitions, particularly when rearranged, may cut off sprinkler distribution so that additional sprinklers are needed.

Narrow spaces between beams and walls or partitions where the construction is combustible.

Loading platforms and other outside structures.

Incomplete sprinkler protection involving one or more of these deficiencies has in the past resulted in a large number of serious fire losses, and in other instances has been the cause of moderate losses which otherwise would have been relatively small if the protection had been complete. Under the current rules allowing from 168 to 200 square feet of area per sprinkler for light hazard occupancy (except for open joisted construction), it is more important than ever to provide *complete* protection.

Construction

Except for light hazard occupancy the present Sprinkler Standard treats all types of construction alike, both as to maximum allowable protected area per sprinkler and as to water supplies. The rules on water supplies entirely ignore the construction except for a bare mention of ceiling construction in one paragraph and a note under a table entitled "Guide to Water Supply Requirements for Sprinkler Systems." According to this note the minimum acceptable water flow for light hazard occupancy may be reduced from 500 gallons per minute to 250 gallons per minute if building is limited in area or if building (including roof) is noncombustible construction.

With respect to sprinkler spacing (maximum area per sprinkler), fire-resistive smooth concrete and combustible roof deck on steel truss are subject to identical restrictions in the case of light hazard occupancy, although there is a very unfavorable comparison for these two types of construction in regard to combustibility, resistance to burn through or collapse, or to the probability of interference with sprinkler distribution, even if the rules are carefully followed with respect to keeping sprinklers away from web or chord members of steel truss.

Furthermore, on the subject of light hazard occupancy, the rules allow up to 200 square feet per sprinkler for smooth ceiling construction but limit the area per sprinkler to 130 square feet for open wood joist construction. The same paragraph in the rules allows a limit of 168 square feet per sprinkler for "all other types of construction." It would seem that this would include a light combustible roof on bar joist. Such a ceiling or roof certainly does not rate very highly from the standpoints of low combustibility and fire resistance.

For ordinary hazard occupancy, which includes nearly all mercantile and manufacturing businesses together with associated warehousing properties, there is no distinction in the water supply rules or in the rules for sprinkler spacing whether the construction is fire-resistive or open wood joist except that a limit of 100 square feet per sprinkler is placed on all buildings housing high-piled storage.

It is difficult to understand the reasoning behind these rules. Truly noncombustible construction cannot add anything to the heat release regardless of any defects in the ability of the system to cope with any probable occupancy fire, and fire-resistive construction will withstand deficiencies in the protection including a temporary interruption of the water supply. It would appear that light combustible construction (wood joist and steel deck on bar-joist or steel truss are good examples) might have better protection from the upper level cooling effect of sprinklers at closer spacing than would be required for the more resistant types of construction.

It must be borne in mind that there is always a chance that deficiencies in the sprinkler system will be present or will occur, that the occupancy may be subject to unfavorable change, or that the system will not always be properly maintained. Under these circumstances, combustible construction will add considerably to the heat release and to the opening of more sprinklers than would be the case with noncombustible construction. Consequently, it seems only reasonable to require a substantial increase in the volume rate of the water supply where combustible construction is involved. Full scale laboratory fire tests under presumably ideal conditions may not indicate the need for an increase in water supply for combustible construction, but unfortunately ideal conditions do not always prevail in practice.

Staggering of Sprinklers

The sprinkler rules for old-style sprinklers required "staggering" of sprinklers (placing sprinklers at alternate locations on adjoining lines) for joisted construction and narrow bay-beam construction in order to insure that the maximum number of channels or bays received some wetting from the sprinkler discharge. With the present standard sprinkler, this reason no longer applies, but there is still some advantage in having the maximum number of channels or bays subject to the atmosphere cooling action of the spray from the sprinklers. What is more important is the need of getting the sprinklers into operation as soon as possible. With open joisted construction or bays with beams on girders, the products of combustion from a fire tend to follow along the joist channels or bays just as water will run in a ditch rather than over its sides. At the same time, travel of hot gases across the joist or beams is very much impeded. Consequently, in order to get the most rapid action from the sprinklers, they should be staggered under all open joist construction and under all bay-beam construction unless the bays are wide enough to have rows of sprinklers in each bay. Since the travel of hot fire gases is faster in channels or bays than across them, the distance between sprinklers in rows across the joist or bays should be kept at the practical minimum.

The present sprinkler rules requires no staggering of sprinklers for light hazard occupancies except under open wood joist where the distance between sprinklers on branch lines exceeds 12 feet. For ordinary hazard occupancies, staggering is required only when the distance between sprinklers on branch lines exceeds 12 feet, and when sprinklers are located directly under solid beams from 3 to 7½ feet apart. There is no excuse with any type of construction for not getting the fastest sprinkler operation possible regardless of occupancy. Therefore, staggering should be done whenever the construction requires it, and the hazards of occupancy should be taken care of primarily by the allowable area per sprinkler and the water supply. It would appear preferable to express a rule as follows: For open wood joist construction and for beam and girder construction, whether of concrete, steel, or wood, staggering is required unless there are sprinklers on branch lines in every bay. The distance between sprinklers on branch lines across joists or beams should not exceed 12 feet in any case, and it is recommended that the spacing of sprinklers on lines across joists or beams be kept nearer the minimum consistent with allowable area per sprinkler. The distance between sprinklers on lines under pitched roofs where the lines are parallel to the peak of the roof should also not exceed 12 feet, and preferably should be less. If the sprinkler lines are perpendicular to the peak then the lines should be not more than 12 feet apart.

Assessment of Occupancy Hazard

There may be considerable variation in hazard even in the same general class of occupancy. Most of the situations and conditions which would warrant special consideration as compared to the occupancy in a general sense are pointed out in the sections of the Sprinkler Standard on "Classification of Occupancies" and "Important Factors in Applying Water Supply Requirements." There are, however, certain instances especially for manufacturing and warehouse occupancies where combustibles may be present in such a wide variety of properties and physical arrangements that it would be well nigh impossible to list all of the conditions which might add to the hazard, either general or localized. In assessing the fire hazard of occupancy there is no good substitute for training and experience, combined with a thorough understanding of the factors which affect growth, spread, and intensity of fires.

Several years ago large-scale storage of automobile tires was judged an "ordinary" hazard. Later, when one manufacturer proposed to store tires on wood pallets 10 feet and more high, an alert inspector questioned the hazard. As a result, large-scale fire tests were run, and it was finally concluded that tire storage was a special hazard calling for increased sprinkler discharge density for protection; not only for multitier pallet storage but even for tires piled on the floor only 6 to 8 feet high. Other similar situations have developed over the years, and there will probably be more in the future.

Water Supplies

The Sprinkler Standard contains a good general guide on the subject of water supplies in Section 2100. The guide is based primarily on occupancy which is divided into six classes: "light" hazard, "ordinary" hazard subdivided into three groups, "woodworkers," and "extra" hazard. In addition, it points out that there are other factors which need consideration: combustibility of contents, height of stock piles, ceiling heights, obstructions to distribution, type of ceiling construction, unprotected openings, unfavorable draft conditions, size of undivided areas, and allowance for hose streams.

Inspection agencies generally have rules for water supplies which take these same factors into consideration, but they may lay more stress on their own long-term experience with various types of constructions and sizes of areas. Some agencies have found that more sprinklers may open when the construction is combustible, a situation requiring larger water supplies. But the principal variation governing the number of sprinklers that may open is the size of the areas involved; the larger the areas, the larger the number that will open on an average. However, the percentage of the total number of sprinklers to open in a single area becomes less a matter of probability as the size of the area is increased. Some credit is usually given to subdivision of areas by walls or partitions which do not meet standards for fire walls, because, except for the flimsiest combustible construction, they do slow down lateral heat and fire spread and tend to make a marked reduction in the number of sprinklers that open.

In considering the time period over which the water supply may be needed, such factors as the persistence of flaming fire and smoldering and the influence of smoke in obscuring visibility must be taken into account. These factors are usually present in fires involving baled cotton or paper and in large-scale storage of automobile tires. The smoky persistent nature of the cotton bale fire is well known so that storehouses for that commodity are generally restricted in area.

Ideas on the proper strength of water supplies undergo some change and modification as new experience is added to the old. Some changes are a result of new experience with old conditions. Other changes are brought about by new practices in manufacturing and warehousing. Within the last 20 to 30 years there has been a considerable increase in the size of areas undivided by fire walls with a corresponding increase in the potential for very large fire losses. At the same time there has been a trend toward single-story construction making use of insulated steel decking on lightweight supports. For a while the fire hazard of insulated steel deck, particularly that employing multilayer membranes with asphalt, was not appreciated. The modern very lightweight bar-joist type of deck support is especially vulnerable to collapse from the heat of a fire without adequate control.

Another change in warehousing practice has added to the fire hazard. This change is due to increased use of lift trucks and cranes, permitting piling of stock to previously unattainable heights. To allow proper headroom for crane operation, ceiling heights may be found from 50 to 80 feet above the floor. These excessive ceiling heights compound the hazard of high piling because, in the event of fire, sprinkler operation is very much delayed while the fire grows and spreads laterally, and the penetration of water down through the fire draft suffers because of the distance which the drops must travel to reach the burning combustible.

The unfavorable conditions attached to high ceilings have been recognized in the case of aircraft hangars, and special rules have been formulated calling for heavy water supplies, and in many cases faster operation of sprinklers through the use of rate-of-rise actuating systems. Two fires of record, each resulting in very large losses, have occurred in storage of rolled paper. In one instance the rolls were stacked on end to heights of 15 to 20 feet or more under a ceiling about 50 feet high to accommodate handling by a traveling crane. These are examples of situations which call for water supplies of very generous amount, because all or nearly all of the sprinklers in the area may open.

Obstruction to Water Distribution

The installation of an automatic sprinkler system represents a considerable investment, and it is important that all reasonable steps be taken to insure that it works effectively and efficiently. Consequently, care must be taken to avoid obstructions to distribution which would render the protection ineffective, at least in part. Soon after the standard sprinkler was adopted for general use in 1954, installation rules were drawn up to prevent serious interference with distribution from the sprinklers by beams and girders. These rules were the result of a careful study of the normal distribution pattern of the new sprinkler, and were designed to maintain at least 95 per cent of the sprinkler's maximum effectiveness. The application of the rules with respect to other types of construction and to fixtures deserves some comment.

The current sprinkler rules (Section 4300) require a separation of 6 inches from bar-joist members (presumably of dimension not over 1 inch). For steel truss, sprinklers should be at least 1 foot laterally from members (web or chord) 4 inches or less in width, and 2 feet laterally from members more than 4 inches wide. For timbers and uprights it is stated that sprinklers should be so located or spaced that any interference is held to a minimum, ordinarily meaning a distance of at least 12 inches. ("Uprights" presumably include columns and posts.) These rules are not entirely consistent within themselves, and for maximum clarity should be more specific.

It would seem to be somewhat better to state these rules as follows:

"All structural members below the level of sprinkler deflectors should be no closer to any sprinkler than six times the dimension (width) of the member. When this requirement calls for a separation of more than 48 inches, the ratio may be reduced to four to one except that the 48-inch separation must be maintained." This rule would include bar-joist, steel or wood truss, columns, posts, diagonal bracing, sprinkler and service piping, and hangers. Horizontal (usually bottom) chord members of steel truss are now covered by the rule for position of sprinkler deflectors with respect to bottoms of beams.

The reason for reducing the separation ratio for distances over 48 inches is that with closer spacing there is usually more than one structural member offering obstruction to distribution and the effect is additive. There is nothing sacrosanct about the six to one ratio or the change in ratio at 48 inches. As a matter of fact there may be good practical reasons for some slight change, but it would appear wise to maintain the six to one ratio for members at least up to 6 inches in width. In any event, no sprinkler should be placed closer than 6 inches to any obstruction, and it would be preferable that a 12-inch minimum be recommended if not required.

A paragraph in the rules states that sprinklers may be located directly above a girder with the top flange not more than 8 inches wide, in which case the deflectors should be at least 6 inches above the top of the girder. This paragraph is probably a holdover from the previous rules for the old-style sprinkler which had a very heavy discharge at points close to the sprinkler. The new standard sprinkler, however, has a fairly uniform discharge up to a radius of about 6 to 7 feet but may be somewhat light in discharge density close to the sprinkler. Consequently, there would be little runoff from the girder to wet combustibles below; instead the girder at this close spacing might seriously impair the distribution. The paragraph should not be retained unless large-scale fire tests show it to be practical.

chapter 15

SUMMARY AND CONCLUSIONS

In the protection of an occupancy of ordinary combustibles against fire, the principal objectives are to extinguish or control the fire by discharging water onto the combustibles, to protect surrounding combustibles and equipment by wetting and cooling, to protect the building construction, and to perform these tasks with the minimum number of sprinklers opened so as to prevent unnecessary water damage. The more important factors to keep in mind in order to accomplish these purposes are:

Water Discharge Density

While this is usually figured as the average discharge from the sprinklers per square foot of floor area, it must be remembered that practically all of the benefit comes from the water which actually reaches the burning combustibles. This is the *effective* discharge density. Assuming that standard sprinklers are used, discharge density can be increased by closer spacing of sprinklers, by the use of large-orifice sprinklers, or by greater water pressure at the sprinklers. Where there is a considerable distance between the sprinklers and the combustibles, it may be impractical to use high sprinkler flowing pressures in order to increase effective discharge density. It would be more effective to use low pressures (15 to 20 pounds per square inch) combined with close sprinkler spacing.

With respect to large-scale tests to determine sprinkler density needed for high-piled stock and other special hazards, it should be kept in mind that sprinkler water penetration down to combustibles is adversely affected by the distance between sprinklers and the combustibles and by the water pressure on the sprinklers. The greater the distance and the higher the water pressure the less the effective penetration. Another factor to keep in mind is the effect on fire intensity when tests are run in structures of restricted area and volume. Under these conditions there may be a considerable return of oxygen deficient gases to the fire zone reducing the fire intensity and leading to false conclusions about the minimum needed sprinkler water density. The use of generous roof hatches is of great help in preventing an unrealistic return of products of combustion. As has been suggested previously in this work on the subject of clearances between sprinklers and combustibles, it is quite risky to assume that favorable results in tests run at a 10-foot clearance would be valid for a clearance of 20 feet, for example.

Sprinkler Flowing Pressure

As the flowing pressure on a sprinkler is increased, the water discharged from the sprinkler increases in proportion to the square root of the pressure. At the same time the lateral range or reach of the discharge is increased, and the break-up or atomization is also increased. Increased atomization of the water results in better atmosphere cooling within the range of the water drops. With respect to range, the length and velocity of travel of a water drop depends on the mass and initial velocity of the drop. The frictional resistance to travel by a drop depends on the drop's surface area. Since small drops have a higher ratio of surface to mass, their comparative range is reduced. If a drop must travel down through a strong fire draft, it is also slowed down by the upward velocity of the fire gases, and simultaneously the drop size is continually being reduced by evaporation.

The flowing pressure on sprinklers is governed by the characteristics of the water supply (relation of pressure to flow), the number of sprinklers that are open and their location with respect to the sprinkler riser, the size and lengths of piping between the riser and the sprinklers, and the condition of the piping interior, whether relatively new and clean or old and reduced in diameter by scale. Of course the elevation of the sprinklers above the water mains supplying the sprinkler system is an important factor. Where it is desired to discharge water and have it reach the combustibles, it is in general not economical to design a sprinkler system for sprinkler flowing pressures over 30 pounds per square inch at the sprinklers with multiple sprinkler operation (20 sprinklers or more). Exceptions would be cases where extra upper level cooling may be needed, such as for flammable liquid exposures, or for ordinary combustibles within 7 to 10 feet from the sprinklers. If the combustibles are within 3 to 5 feet of the sprinklers, pressures as high as 50 pounds per square inch or even more would afford improved protection. Where pressures in the higher range are advisable for the conditions, it is usually better to increase the sprinkler system feed pipe sizes rather than to install high pressure pumps (rated at 150 pounds per square inch or more for full flow), although occasionally high pressure pumps may be needed when the sprinklers are located at considerable elevations above the yard system.

Water Supply Volume Rate

The water supply volume rate or maximum gallons per minute at good pressure that is required at a property is generally determined by the large loss experience that has occurred under somewhat similar conditions of construction and occupancy. The objective is to have available for the sprinkler system, above any extraneous drain such as hose streams, sufficient water to supply all the sprinklers which might reasonably be expected to open at an effective flowing pressure. For some types of hazard or under some conditions it is probable that all of the sprinklers in the area would open in the event of fire. In general the probable expectancy is some fraction of the total number of sprinklers, the fraction increasing as the size of the area is reduced.

While the current sprinkler rules do not ask for heavier

water supplies where the construction is combustible, it does not appear reasonable that there should be no difference in the requirement. Consequently, it seems advisable to make an extensive check of fire losses with and without combustible construction before the rules can be justified.

While the current sprinkler rules mention "type of ceiling construction" as a primary factor in determining the number of sprinklers expected to operate, there is no specific guide to help the system designer in determining the effect of combustible construction on the probable number of sprinklers which might open. It is quite possible that a careful study of comparative loss experience would indicate an increase of 25 per cent or even more for combustible construction as compared to noncombustible construction.

Ceiling Heights

This is one of the primary factors mentioned in the sprinkler rules for consideration in determining recommended water supplies. However, it seems that the importance of this factor has not always been properly recognized. The effectiveness of any sprinkler system is decreased with clearance between sprinklers and combustibles over 5 to 10 feet and also is decreased with increasing severity of any possible fire. A particularly striking example is a situation involving high-piled combustible storage combined with the very generous clearances required for traveling crane operation. On the other hand, the sprinklers operate to best advantage over ordinary combustibles without high piling and with clearances around the order of 3 to 5 feet. With the smaller clearances more water from the sprinklers reaches the combustibles and at the same time there is some added advantage in the return of oxygen deficient products of combustion to the fire zone.

Obstructions

It seems hardly necessary to say much about this factor because it should be obvious that, in order for a sprinkler to operate at maximum effectiveness, there should be no interference with its distribution. The wider the spacing between sprinklers the more important this factor becomes. Where there is serious interference to distribution a fire has a chance for additional growth, resulting in the opening of more sprinklers with attendant water damage and possibly resulting in a large loss instead of a small one.

Fire Stopping

There is a definite advantage in fire stopping joisted construction at intervals not over 30 feet, and in framing beams into girders to form panels. Prompt operation of sprinklers is more certain, and, if the ceiling is combustible, the retention of oxygen deficient gases in the channels or bays tends to reduce the rate of combustion of the ceiling.

Draft Curtains and Heat Vents

Draft curtains are valuable in preventing or delaying the spread of heat beyond the immediate fire area, the extent of the delay being roughly proportional to the enclosed volume of the curtained area. On account of the turbulent motion of fire gases, curtains 1 to 2 feet deep are of little value. Curtains 5 to 6 feet deep are more practical. Curtains over 6 feet deep are especially needed for fires above average intensity and duration. When combined with open or automatic heat vents of the proper size, draft curtains may confine the heat of relatively severe fires of long duration. Heat vents alone without draft curtains are of dubious value.

Draft curtains and heat vents are particularly useful in preventing the spread of heat from hazardous operations such as those involving handling of flammable liquids. They may also be of great value for the subdivision of large fire areas where firewalls are impractical, especially in buildings which have combustible ceilings. If the fire curtains are reasonably deep and the vents of adequate ratio for the hazard, the combination will not only prevent the opening of excessive numbers of sprinklers but will also dissipate most of the smoke which would otherwise seriously interfere with manual fire fighting efforts. One objection to the provision of automatic vents of effective area is the expense involved. This is usually greater in a flat roof without monitors than in one with monitors which add to the stack effect of fire curtains and which can ordinarily be fitted with vents more economically.

Sprinkler Operating Speed and Temperature Rating

A low temperature rating for one sprinkler does not necessarily mean that it will operate faster than another with a higher rating. Speed of response depends primarily on the ratio of surface area to mass of the fuse link or other actuating element. Where this ratio is the same, sprinklers of lower temperature rating will operate in a shorter length of time, but under some fire conditions a fast sprinkler of 212°F. rating may operate sooner than a slow sprinkler of 160°F. or even 135°F. rating. Furthermore, the low temperature sprinklers are somewhat more likely to operate prematurely from high but normal room temperature conditions. This is well borne out by sprinkler leakage experience barring incidents due to mechanical injury or freezing.

A study was made of all fires involving sprinkler protection in Factory Mutual insured plants over a 5-year period — about 6,000 fires in all. Complete failures of protection or fires obviously out of control for one reason or another were excluded; fires in textile occupancy were analyzed separately. It was found that where all of the sprinklers involved were of 212°F. temperature rating the number of sprinklers that opened per fire was less than for sprinklers of ordinary degree rating (160°F. to 165°F.). There were not enough fires with sprinklers above 212°F. rating to have any statistical significance. Oddly enough, for the ordinary temperature rating there was no great difference between fast sprinklers and slow sprinklers in the number of sprinklers that opened.

Since most all fires in commercial and industrial properties burn vertically at a much faster rate than the horizontal or lateral travel, it would be expected for this class of fire that fewer sprinklers would open if of higher than ordinary temperature rating. Some full scale laboratory tests tend to confirm this tentative conclusion. On the other hand, for fires in fuzzy textile fibers or for fires in ordinary combustibles under high ceilings, the temperature buildup at the ceiling would be slower and at the same time more widespread, indicating an advantage for sprinklers of lower temperature rating. Again, the loss experience analysis did not confirm this theory, although the numbers of fires under these conditions were somewhat scant for a significant conclusion.

Based on theoretical considerations alone, it would appear that sprinklers with higher than ordinary temperature operating points and with low thermal inertia (fast sprinklers) would have a decided advantage in reducing water damage by keeping down the number of sprinklers operating per fire, particularly for the usual fire which does not spread laterally except at a slow rate. Full scale tests on a simulated festooned paper dryer showed a very marked advantage for the fast sprinklers, and other tests on fires in wood cribs show fewer sprinklers opened with the higher temperature rated sprinklers. To determine just what is the optimum temperature operating point for sprinklers is an intriguing problem. Possibly the best sprinkler would be one with fast response but with the operating temperature raised to 185°F. or higher. For fires with fast upward travel and of high intensity, i.e., high-piled stock with many vertical spaces, there may be advantages in using sprinklers with temperature ratings as high as 286°F. No final decision can be made without many full scale tests under varying conditions of occupancy and ceiling height plus at least some experience on selected occupancies.

Replacement of Old-Style Sprinklers

In properties equipped with old-style sprinklers, where there is the problem of improving sprinkler protection while at the same time reducing potential water damage, there is no other way in which so much improvement can be obtained per dollar of cost than by replacing the old-style sprinklers with standard sprinklers. A great number of full scale fire tests under widely varying conditions have shown reductions in number of sprinklers opened with the same water supply from 33 per cent to as high as 75 per cent. Other tests have shown equal or better efficiency at flowing pressures reduced by 40 per cent or more. This means that a standard sprinkler can be expected to do as good a job at 3 pounds per square inch water pressure as an old-style sprinkler at 5 pounds per square inch.

Sprinkler leakage loss experience (premature operation of a single sprinkler with no fire) shows average loss per opened sprinkler of about $1,000. This figure has steadily moved upward over the years as a dollar buys fewer goods and services. This figure is based on losses in all kinds of occupancies, so that it would be undoubtedly much higher if restricted to those occupancies obviously subject to high water damage. Losses by fire in industrial properties run around the order of magnitude of $500 per sprinkler. What portion of this is water damage is not known, but the proportion is no doubt fairly high for small fires involving less than ten sprinklers. If, by replacing old-style sprinklers with standard sprinklers, the number of sprinklers opened on the average can be reduced from six to four, the water damage reduction per fire might probably run around $500. For occupancies known to be especially susceptible to water damage the saving would be much greater.

As a result of these considerations there cannot be any valid argument against replacement of old-style sprinklers where the strength of the water supply is somewhat scant or in locations known to be particularly susceptible to water damage.

Completeness of Protection

In order to be sure of the effectiveness of any sprinkler system it must be complete. This means that all locations of the building and all process equipment in which fire might occur should be sprinklered. These locations include conveyer openings between floors, hoods over process equipment, under platforms, mezzanine floors and walkways, air conditioning and dust collecting systems, large ventilation or exhaust ducts if combustible or containing combustible dusts or deposits, ovens and dryers if combustibles are present, long cutting tables over 4 feet wide, spaces above false ceilings and under first floors if combustible construction or contents are present, and the interiors of wide storage racks especially over 12 feet high.

SUBJECT INDEX

Combustibility, *continued*
  of preservative treatments, 4
  of pyroxylin plastic, 7
Combustible construction
  adds to occupancy hazard, 125
  sprinkler spacing for, 127
Combustible gases, 10; *see also*
  Gases, combustible
Combustible liquids, 9; *see also*
  Flammable liquids
Combustible solids, *see also*
  Solids, combustible
  fuel properties, 1
  high-piled, effect on fire
    intensity of, 46
Combustion products, *see*
  Products of combustion
Conduction, heat losses by, 71
Conductivity
  hydrogen, 12
  magnesium, 12
Congreve, William, early
  sprinkler patents, 74
Cooling
  the atmosphere, 85
  burning combustibles, 84
  exposed elements, 86
Cousins, E. W., *The FM
  Construction Materials
  Calorimeter*, 39

D

Decomposition, thermal, 17
Discharge density, from
  sprinklers, 141
Distribution density, sprinkler
  discharge, 105
Distribution patterns
  old-style sprinklers, 77
  standard sprinklers, 77
  tests of, 78
Draft curtains
  effect of, 145
  at hazardous locations, 145
  subdivision of areas by, 145
"Duraspeed" sprinklers, 75

E

Ethylene, 10

Exposures, protection of
  by automatic sprinklers, 86,
    111
  by directed spray, 115
Extinguishment
  by cooling, 84
  by wetting, 84
Extra hazards, water supply for,
  119, 136

F

Factory Mutual construction
  materials calorimeter, 25, 31,
  39, 46, 71
The Factory Mutuals, 1835-1935,
  Manufacturers Mutual Fire
  Insurance Company, 73
Factory Mutual Engineering
  Division, *Handbook of
  Industrial Loss Prevention*, 15
Failures, sprinkler systems, 130
Fibers
  animal, 6
  synthetic textiles, 6
  vegetable, 5
Fir plank ceiling, fire tests of, 32
Fire, a vapor-phase reaction, 1
Fire breaks, noncombustible, 70
Fire characteristic, ignition as
  a, 16
Fire draft, 104
Fire intensity
  defined, 34
  effect of air supply on, 36
  effect of exposure temperature
    on, 46
  effect of fire stopping on, 41
  effect of height of combustibles
    on, 41, 46
  effect of oxygen deficient
    atmospheres on, 38, 40
  effect of physical state of fuel
    on, 35
  effect of radiation on, 42
  effect of specific surface on, 36
  effect of temperature on, 38
Fire loading, 21
Fire losses, industrial, 73
Fire points, defined, 13
Fire retardant treatments
  impregnations, 4
  paints, 5

Fire spread, *see* Flame spread
Fire stopping, effect of, 41, 126, 145
Fire tests
    clearances, ceiling to sprinklers, 97
    combustion products, extinguishment by, 88
    fir plank ceilings, 32
    insulated steel deck roofs, 32
    joisted wood construction, 122
    occupancy hazards, 124
    operating times of sprinklers, 91
    panel construction, 101
    protection against exposures, 111
    smooth ceilings, under, 97
    spray nozzles, effect of, 115
    sprinklers
        discharge at different pressures, 106
        discharge through fire draft, 104
        operating times, 93
        standard sprinklers, 80
    steel decks with no asphalt adhesive, 32
    wood roofs, 28
Flames
    horizontal spread of, 22
    nonluminous, 41
    as vapor phase reactions, 22
    vertical spread of, 22
    visibility of, 22
Flame spread
    explained, 21
    over steel deck roofs, 30
    over wood ceilings, 25
    over wood structures, 24
Flammable liquids
    atomized combustion, 9
    as fuels, 9
Flash points, defined, 13
Fluorine, reactivity of, 15
Foam rubber, as a fuel, 8
Francis, James B., early sprinkler systems, 74
Fuel properties
    auto-oxidation, 13
    of combustibles, 1

fire points, 13
flash points, 13
heat conductivity, 12
heat of combustion, 12
heat of decomposition, 11
heat of fusion, 11
heat of vaporization, 11
instability, 14
melting point, 11
moisture content, 14
nature of, 15
physical state, 10
reactivity, 14
specific heat, 12
spontaneous heating, 13
volatility, 10

G

Gases, combustible
    acetylene, 10
    ammonia, 10
    butane, 10
    carbon monoxide, 10
    ethylene, 10
    hydrogen, 10
    liquefied petroleum, 10
    methane, 10
    natural gas, 10
    propylene, 10
Germanium, 8
Girders, effect on operating times of sprinklers, 101
"Glass button" sprinklers, 75
Globe "Saveall" sprinklers, 75
Glowing fires, 23
Grinnell
    "Duraspeed" sprinklers, 75
    "quartz bulb" sprinklers, 75

H

Hafnium, 8
Hay, spontaneous heating of, 13
Hazardous locations, draft curtains for, 145
Heat
    of combustion, 12
    conduction, losses by, 71
    conductivity, 12
    of decomposition, 11